ELECTRONIC
SENSING CONTROLS

ELECTRONIC SENSING CONTROLS

by Steven E. Summer

CHILTON BOOK COMPANY

Philadelphia   New York   London

pd
b-29-89

To Barbara

Acknowledgment is due to G. Kousourou, Assistant Professor, Department of Electrical Technology, Queensboro Community College, New York City, for his painstaking technical review of the manuscript. I also wish to thank the many firms who have contributed technical data and photographs.

Preface

Electronic Sensing Controls presents the fundamentals of a large class of industrial electronics equipment. Sensing controls automate simple processes such as counting, sorting, measuring, and detecting. Freeing the worker from undesirable tasks, they perform jobs which would be impossible for human abilities.

This book may be divided into three sections. The first, comprising Chapters 1-3, provides a review of common technology and electronics. In Chapter 2 the properties of many commonly used sensors and transducers are covered and compared. The selection of devices was necessarily limited to those most commonly used. Chapter 3 reviews basic electronic circuitry relevant to the subject, including semiconductor diodes, transistors, and integrated circuits. Schematic drawings of simple circuits facilitate the reader's comprehension of the properties of frequently used circuits. Also, useful generic circuits, comparators, differential and operational amplifiers, Schmitt triggers, and monostable multivibrators are discussed.

The second section, Chapters 4-6, is arranged according to basic types of controls. These include photoelectric, temperature-sensitive, and mechanical controls. Each type of control is thoroughly discussed in relation to its numerous uses. I have selected only three basic families of controls, in order to make the material more cohesive.

Chapter 7 investigates the effects of feedback on sensing controls. First, the effects of feedback on a purely electronic system are calculated. Then a similar analysis is performed on an electromechanical system, illustrating the similarities between the two feedback systems.

These analyses do not take into account the dynamic response of non-elementary systems, which, requiring a knowledge of differential equations, are beyond the scope of this book.

STEVEN E. SUMMER

Contents

1

Principles of Electronic Sensing Controls

An *electronic sensing control* makes decisions electronically in response to phenomena which affect a sensor. The output of the sensing control may be used to modify the sensed phenomena, or it may be used for other purposes. Regardless of how the control is used, the result will be a saving of human labor, or the accomplishment of a task that is too difficult or too tedious for human labor. The term "electronic sensing control" embraces many types of familiar electronic equipment, such as the photoelectric control, the temperature control, and the motor speed control. Many uncommon controls, such as ultrasonic, thermal, and infrared controls, may also be included in the category. All of these controls have a common basis, and so are related.

Essentially, an electronic sensing control may be envisioned as a combination of three basic blocks. The first element is the *sensor* or *transducer*. The sensor or transducer bridges the gap between the environment and the electronic circuitry of the control. Since this is the only connection between the sensed phenomena and the electronic circuits, its performance and characteristics are very important, and determine the performance of the control to a large degree. The in-

11

put of the sensor may be any physical quantity such as light, heat, pressure, force, or velocity. The output of the sensor may be a voltage or current. An alternative output is a change in an electrical quantity, which may be resistance, capacitance, or inductance. These changes may be easily converted to corresponding voltages or currents. Two different types of sensors are available for virtually every application. The first type of sensor has an output which corresponds to the input. It will not be linear, or follow any well defined pattern. There may be a large performance variation from unit to unit. The main attributes of this type of sensor are its sensitivity and its repeatability. We expect that the output will be roughly proportional to the input. More important, we will always get the same output for the same input conditions. This means that the desired condition may be set up, and the response of the sensor may then be calibrated for one or two points of operation. Once calibrated, it will perform consistently at the point or points of calibration.

The second type of sensor also has an output which corresponds to the input. However, this correspondence is either linear, or faithfully obeys some other mathematical law. It has a well defined transfer function from physical input to electrical output. There may be considerable uniformity from sensor to sensor. Unfortunately, the linearity of this sensor may be obtained at the expense of output amplitude. This type of sensor may be referred to as a transducer because of its well defined transfer function.

There may be a considerable difference in sensitivity between the two types of sensors. By "sensitivity" we mean the output change for a given input change. The first kind of sensor generally has a very high sensitivity. This may simplify its associated circuitry. The second type usually has an insensitive output, and often considerable circuitry must be added to obtain a useful amplitude.

The second element of the sensing control is the necessary electronic *circuitry*. What is necessary depends on the type of sensor, the required results, and the proper output. The task of the electronic circuitry is threefold. First, it must act as a signal conditioner for the sensor. This may mean that the sensor output has to be converted to some desired voltage or current. Amplification may also be necessary. The sensor output may have to be normalized, or referenced to a specific voltage, current, or input quantity. Signal conditioning includes all that is necessary to make the sensor's output usable. The second function of the circuitry is to perform some form of mathematical operation on the conditioned sensor output. This may be to determine whether the sensor signal is greater than, or less than, some arbitrary limit. The circuitry may also be used to perform addition, subtraction, multiplication, division, integration, or differentiation of the sensor signal. Lastly, after the sensor signal has been acted upon, the circuitry must translate the results to an appropriate output. This may be an amplified signal, an error voltage, the gating of an SCR (silicon-controlled rectifier), or the closing of relay contacts. Whatever the output, the circuitry must act as an interface.

The final block is the *output actuator*. This is the device which performs the tasks directed by the electronic circuitry. It is the muscle of the sensing control. Some common output actuators are electric motors, solenoids, relays, heater coils, transistors, SCR's, and electrically operated valves and other mechanisms.

A block diagram of a typical electronic sensing control is shown in Fig. 1-1.

The Decision-Making Control

The electronic sensing control is used largely to make decisions. The basis for these decisions is the input from the sensor. The manner of the decision may be go–no go, yes or

Fig. 1-1 A block diagram of a typical electronic sensing control composed of a sensor, the necessary circuitry, and an output device.

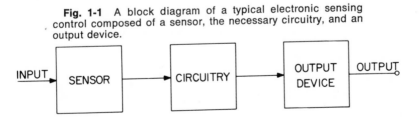

no, or more or less. These decisions are programmed into the control by its construction. The point at which action is taken may be internally or externally set. To illustrate, consider a temperature controller. Its internal programming may be set up as follows. First, convert temperature to voltage. Compare this voltage, which corresponds to temperature, to a reference voltage. If the difference is negative, close the contacts of the output relay. If it is positive, open the contacts of the relay. Clearly, the control here is making a decision about the magnitude of the sensed temperature. Depending on the relation between the actual temperature and the desired temperature, an action will be taken.

A similar type of control is the motor under-speed or over-speed control. With this type of control, an indication or action follows when the speed of a motor exceeds or is less than a certain speed. This type of control is clearly a sensing control because the motor speed is being acted upon and sensed. Such a control may work by generating a voltage proportional to motor speed, and then comparing it to a reference voltage. The comparison is easily made by subtracting one quantity from the other, and operating on the polarity of the difference. Depending on the polarity of the difference, the motor speed indicated may or may not be satisfactory.

If it is desired to keep a certain sensed quantity constant, the output of the control may be used for this purpose. The control will sense when the quantity is not within limits, and effect a correction. This action is called inverse or negative feedback, because the results are being fed back to the input to modify the same results. While most indicating controls or alarm controls require only an on–off type of output, this may not suffice for feedback controls. An on–off control allows only two states; it requires either corrective action or no corrective action at all. If only a small amount of corrective action is required, an excessive amount may be taken because the control cannot regulate the amount of action required. This overcompensation may indeed lead to large differences between desired and actual results. A reasonable output must be proportional to the amount of correction necessary. That is, if a large amount of correction is needed, the output must be larger than it is when a small amount of correction is required. This necessitates a linear feedback control. Such a control might still make a comparison between the input and a reference. However, the output would now be a function of the amount of difference between the two, as well as of polarity of the difference. Linear feedback controls are most often used when some quantity is to be kept constant. Not only is the performance usually better than with two state controls, but the results can be easily predicted with simple mathematical relationships.

There is a clear distinction between sensing controls with a linear output and conditioned sensors. The output of the sensing control is not the conditioned signal from the sensor, but it is the signal from the sensor which has been operated upon. The output of a sensing control with a linear response is used to modify the input, and is thus a signal within a negative feedback loop. While the conditioned signal from a sensor may accomplish the actions of a sensing control with the addition of circuitry and components, it is not a sensing control by itself.

There are many different kinds of sensing controls. This is partially due to the large number of applications, and also to the variety of methods which may be employed to accomplish the desired aims. The controls may be grouped according to the tasks they perform, or they may be grouped according to the means they use to operate. In this book, sensing controls will be discussed in the latter way. Classification by similarities in the operation of the controls allows the description of each method to be more thorough and avoids repetition. The operation of each type of sensing control will depend largely on the type of transducer used, and on the nature of the input. Therefore, the controls are logically treated when grouped together according to the inputs to which the sensors respond. In this book we will separately discuss photoelectric, temperature, and mechanical inputs, as well as feedback controls. Although the last category may include the first three, feedback controls are so widely used that they merit further discussion.

2

Sensors and Transducers

The *sensor* or *transducer* is the device which bridges the gap between nonelectrical phenomena and electrical circuitry. Because electrical circuitry may be made to provide great linearity, sensitivity, and versatility, the sensor or transducer is the element in the chain which actually determines the performance of the sensing system. The quality of the sensor usually determines the quality of the sensing control as well. Occasionally an output device will also limit the control's performance, but this is generally in an area where improvement is available.

The words "sensor" and "transducer" denote a device which responds to a physical phenomenon and translates certain attributes of the phenomenon into an electrical property, which a circuit may process further. The sensor or transducer must be sensitive to one thing only, but all physical devices are sensitive to many phenomena. Therefore we need devices which have strong sensitivity to one phenomenon and very little sensitivity to all extraneous phenomena. For example, some desirable qualities of a light sensor are *insensitivity* to temperature, pressure, moisture, radiation, and vibration. If we cannot get a sensor or transducer with these insensitivities, then we try to minimize them by some form of compensation.

The sensor or transducer may have to respond to either the quality or the quantity of the physical phenomena. A light sensor will respond both to the amount of incident light falling upon it, and to the color of that light. It is possible that one or the other sensitivity may be desired. For example, a control which monitors the *color* of a dyed fabric should not be sensitive to the *amount* of light reflected from it.

The output of the sensor or transducer may be related to the sensed phenomena linearly or nonlinearly. The sensitivity of a device may be computed by dividing a small increment of the output quantity by a corresponding increment of the input quantity. If the sensitivity is fairly constant for wide ranges of the input phenomena, then the response is linear, and the device is generally termed a transducer. If the response is nonlinear, then the device may be called a sensor. Since linearity is relative, all transducers are also sensors. The value of a linear sensor is that the response for any input may be predicted if the sensitivity (the slope of the input–output curve) and the response at one point are known. Since electric circuits are, or can be made, predominantly linear, the designer of the control can more easily predict the performance when given a linear sensor.

The response of the sensor is an electrical property. It may be a voltage or a current, a resistance, capacitance, inductance or impedance. It may be a time-varying voltage, a periodic voltage, or a random voltage. Regardless of its form, the electrical circuits will modify it, amplify it, shape it, and use it to control an output device. The electrical properties of the sensor are intimately bound up with its physical properties. Naturally, the easier the electrical properties are to work with, the more desirable is the sensor for use in electronic sensing controls. Few sensors can deliver enough power to actuate output devices directly. Most of them must receive some form of amplification, which implies a vacuum-tube, semiconductor, or magnetic amplifier. Therefore, a valuable quality in a sensor is the ability to work easily with available circuitry. This means reasonable impedance levels, voltage levels, and current levels. If a sensor requires a very high impedance load, or a low-noise amplifier, these circuits must be added to the cost of the sensor, as it is unusable without them.

Another consideration is the repeatability of the sensor. This means two things. First, the sensor should perform the same way day after day. If it must constantly be adjusted, then the sensing control is of little value because of the labor needed to keep it functioning. Second, the sensors should give the same performance from unit to unit. This simplifies the design and manufacture of the sensing control, and eliminates adjustments when the sensor is replaced. The more of an interchangeable part the sensor is, the more the dependent circuitry is simplified.

The sensor interacts with its environment. In so doing it affects or changes the physical phenomena that it attempts to sense. Thus it is desirable for a sensor to affect its environment only in a minimum way. If it senses incident light, it should block off as little light as possible. If it senses a fluid flow, it should impede the flow as little as possible. If temperature is to be measured, the sensor should not contribute to the heat. If motion is sensed, the motion should not be impeded. This property of non-interaction is not related to the sensor's sensitivity. However, the amount of interaction should be kept as slight as possible or the sensor will consume the phenomena it is trying to control.

It is obvious that few sensors can actually meet these performance criteria. Fortunately, few applications require that all the criteria be satisfied. If the sensor can meet the requirements of the application, then it will more than suffice. The designer of a sensing control must first establish the physical phenomena to be sensed and the final output needed from the control. This done, the sensor can be selected in order to meet the input characteristics. Finally, the electronic circuitry which interfaces the sensor and the output device must be designed. The application is the primary determinant of the system's design; the sensor, and finally the electronics, are next in order of importance. The advantage of listing the criteria desirable in all sensors is that the list may be examined with regard to the application, and noncritical qualities discarded. Then the sensor may be selected objectively from the available devices, keeping in mind the manner of electronic circuitry required for use of the sensor.

Fortunately, many sensors and transducers are available. The great number of these devices prevents examination of each in detail. Therefore, we will investigate a few of the more common devices in order to impart some familiarity with what is available and in wide use.

POTENTIOMETERS

Potentiometers are widely used for the measurement of linear and angular displacement. A potentiometer transducer (not to be confused with the voltage-measuring potentiometer) is composed of a resistor with an adjustable tap (see Fig. 2-1). The tap may contact the entire length of the resistor. There are three terminals, of which two are connected to the resistance and the third is the tap. The resistance between the first two terminals is constant, while the resistance between the tap and any other terminal may vary from zero to the total amount. The position of the tap with respect to the

Fig. 2-1 The simple potentiometer: (a) conventional rotary potentiometer; (b) construction of a linear actuation potentiometer; (c) schematic symbol for a potentiometer.

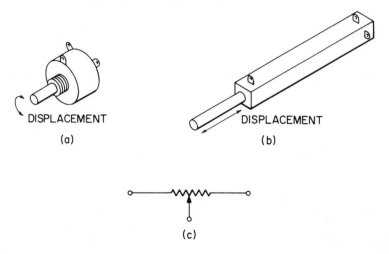

DISPLACEMENT

(a)

DISPLACEMENT

(b)

(c)

resistor is controlled by an arm or shaft. In the rotary potentiometer the resistance is shaped into a cylinder. A shaft in the center of the cylinder rotates a movable arm, or wiper, which contacts the surface of the resistor. The position of the arm is a function of relative angular displacement. The rotary potentiometer can be geared with rack-and-pinion gears in order to measure linear displacement. However, it may be simpler to use a potentiometer whose resistance element is arranged in a linear fashion instead of a cylindrically. Here the position of the tap is directly controlled by linear displacement.

In use, a fixed voltage is applied across the two resistance terminals, so that the resultant voltage at the tap is directly proportional to both the applied voltage and the angular or linear displacement of the shaft. However, if any appreciable current is drawn out of the tap then a Thevinin equivalent circuit of the potentiometer must be used to find the tap voltage. The resistance which the tap feeds should be at least ten times greater than the potentiometer resistance for reasonable accuracy.

The simplest, and historically the oldest, form of the potentiometer was the slide-wire type. The resistance element was a piece of straight wire, and a tap moved along its length. Its disadvantage was its low nominal resistance. In order to realize higher resistances, a long length of wire was needed. To fit this long length of wire into a reasonable size, it was wound around a nonconducting card or form in a helical arrangement. These so-called wirewound potentiometers are widely used. Instead of using wire for the resistance element, a conductive material such as carbon or conductive plastic may be used. With these elements it is possible to achieve a very high resistance between terminals. These potentiometers may have a much higher *resolution* than the wirewound type. Resolution is a measure of how fine an adjustment may be achieved with the potentiometer. The higher the resolution, the more precisely can the position of the tap be placed. With a potentiometer having 0.5 per cent resolution, there are only 200 positions for the tap. The resolution of a wirewound potentiometer depends on the number of turns of wire used. The higher-resistance units have more turns, and consequently a higher resolution, than the lower-resistance units. Carbon potentiometers have a much higher resolution than wirewound types, but compare unfavorably in other areas. The resolution of a carbon potentiometer depends on the granularity of the carbon.

Potentiometers are among the simplest and best transducers for measuring displacements, as they are accurate, linear, and also inexpensive. The torque required to actuate most high quality potentiometers is usually low because of high tolerance, precision construction, and use of ball bearings.

Linear Variable Differential Transformer

The linear variable differential transformer is used to measure displacement. The transformer (abbreviated LVDT) has one primary winding and two secondary windings which are arranged on a common axis (Fig. 2-2). The core is movable, and is connected to a shaft. The two secondaries are connected so that their voltages subtract from one another. When the coupling from the primary to each secondary is equal, the two secondary voltages are equal, and the net output voltage is zero. If the core is moved slightly from this center position, the output voltage will increase.

Since the LVDT is a transformer, the primary must be supplied with an ac voltage. This voltage is commonly under ten volts at 60 Hz to 400 Hz. Because of leakage and mismatched windings, there will be a finite voltage at the null, but this error voltage is usually less than 1 per cent of the full-scale output voltage. The frequency of the primary voltage limits the rate at which the core can be moved.

The output voltage is proportional in magnitude to the displacement of the core from the null position. The phase of the output voltage will change abruptly from 0° to 180° when passing through the null. Thus, if the magnitude and direction of the displacement of the core must be known, then the amplitude and phase of the output must be sensed.

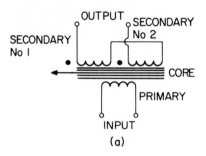

(a)

Fig. 2-2 The linear variable differential potentiometer (LVDT): (a) schematic symbol; (b) cross-sectional view showing placement of coils and movable core; (c) electrical characteristics showing output as a function of displacement of the movable core, with the input voltage constant.

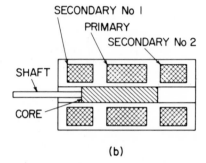

(b)

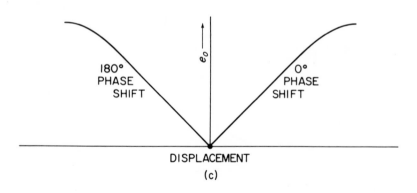

(c)

The phase of the output is referenced to the phase of the primary voltage.

The length of travel for the LVDT can be up to several inches. The magnetic field generated by the primary winding will exert a small force on the core to bring it back to the null position. This force is usually below one gram. Because the LVDT is a magnetic device, it should be kept away from other transformers and magnetic bodies which may cause errors.

STRAIN GAUGES

Strain gauges are the most commonly used transducers for the measurement and control of force. The gauge is usually constructed of wire which exhibits a change in resistance as

Fig. 2-3 Strain gauges: (a) construction of an unbonded wire gauge; (b) construction of a bonded wire gauge; (c—opposite) bonded foil gauges (photo courtesy of BLH Electronics, Inc.).

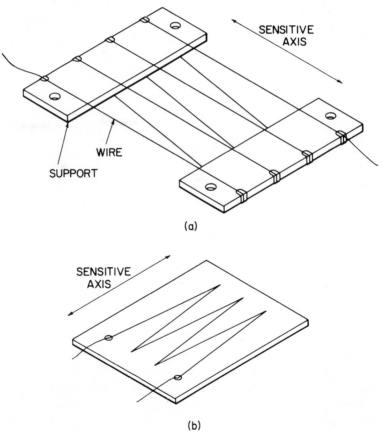

SENSITIVE AXIS

WIRE

SUPPORT

(a)

SENSITIVE AXIS

(b)

a function of strain. (A "strain" is a minute deformation or elongation of a material under applied stress.) Thus, a strain gauge is actually sensitive to deformation rather than force. However, for small changes of stress there will be a corresponding change in strain if the gauge material is in the elastic region. Similarly, the potentiometer, which is displacement sensitive, could be converted to a force-sensitive device by adding a spring to convert force to displacement.

The useful resistance change in the strain gauge may be from 0.1 to 1.0 per cent of the nominal gauge resistance. The nominal resistance is normally under 1000 ohms, but higher resistances can be achieved. The resistance change is so small that a bridge circuit is necessary for its measurement.

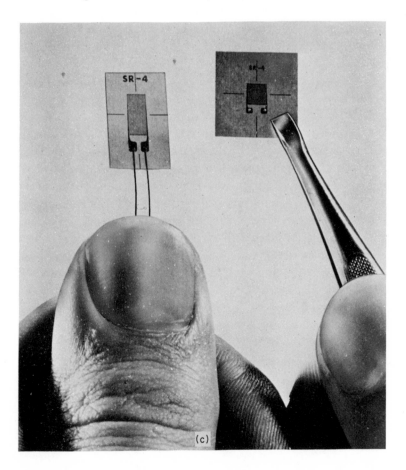

(c)

There are two common types of strain gauge construction, the unbonded and bonded types. The unbonded gauge (Fig. 2-3a) is simply made. A deformation in the sensitive direction will stretch the wires. The wire resistance increases due to a reduction in cross section and an increase in resistivity. The second effect is normally slight. The wire will not stretch appreciably when a deformation is applied perpendicular to the sensitive direction. The gauge will exhibit a high sensitivity in one axis only. This is a very useful feature. A high-resistance wire, such as nichrome, is generally used.

There are several disadvantages of the unbonded strain gauge, including large size, mechanical clumsiness, and the need for an applied stress for "bias." Bonded strain gauges overcome most of the objectionable properties of the unbonded gauge. They are constructed (Figs. 2-3b and c) of a zig-zag of very fine wire which is fastened to a paper base, and which is covered for protection of the element. The gauge is bonded or cemented to the material exhibiting the strain.

Because of the small resistance changes which must be measured, a bridge circuit is mandatory. The strain gauge material is apt to be very sensitive to temperature. However, the temperature sensitivity is easily compensated by using another strain gauge as a bridge element. This gauge, often called a "dummy" gauge, is at the same ambient temperature as the primary gauge, but is not subject to any deformation. The temperature coefficients of the two gauges will track each other, and there will be very little temperature error.

The power dissipated in the gauge should be very small because it will change the gauge's resistance. This limits the magnitude of the bridge output to the millivolt level. To avoid errors due to bridge-amplifier drift, the bridge is often supplied with an ac carrier so that the bridge amplifier can be ac coupled.

PHOTOSENSITIVE CONDUCTORS

A photosensitive conductor is one whose resistance is a function of the intensity of applied light. The resistance may

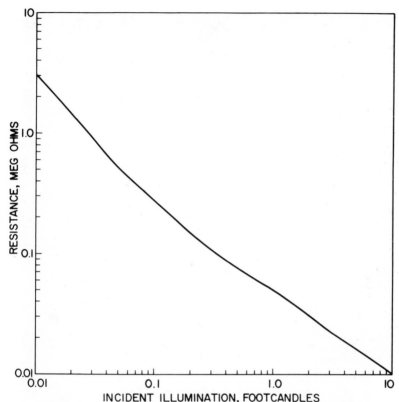

Fig. 2-4 The graph of resistance of a typical photocon-
ductor versus incident light shows highly nonlinear response
and wide resistance change.

also be a function of the light wavelength, the temperature,
and the previous light history of the conductor. Some photo-
conducting materials include germanium, silicon, selenium,
metallic halides, oxides, and sulfides. Of these, the most popular types are made of cadmium sulfide and cadmium selenide.
The conductance of these materials increases with increasing
light intensity, hence their resistance decreases (see Fig. 2-4).
The transfer function is generally nonlinear, but some photoconductive mixtures approach linearity over a limited range.
The incremental linearity (for small changes in light intensity) is reasonable for most photoconductors.

The cells are constructed on a flat surface so that the photoconductive material lies between two conducting strips, which

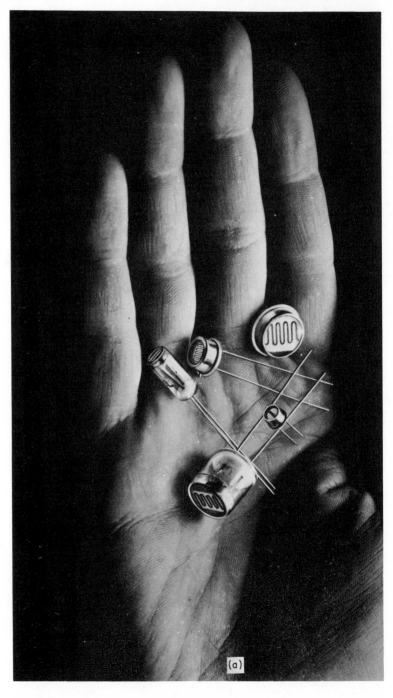

(a)

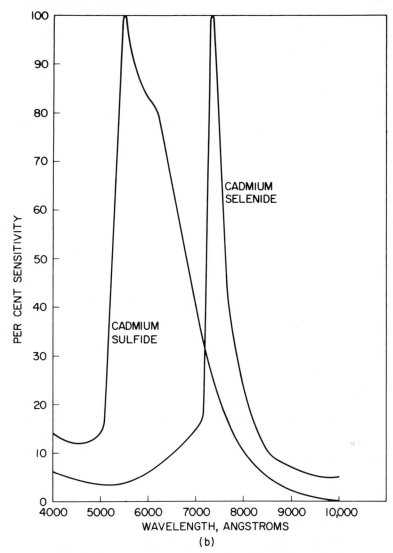

Fig. 2-5 (a—opposite) Typical construction of photocon-
ductor cells (photo courtesy of Clairex Electronics, Inc.); (b)
spectral sensitivity of photoconductors: relative sensitivity as
a function of applied light wavelength in angstroms.

are used as terminals. The conducting strips may be inter-
digitated so that the length of the light-sensitive area is maximized. The cell is then sealed into a case to provide protection
against moisture, corrosives, and dust. A flat, round case is the

most common configuration, but rectangular styles are also used.

A photosensitive resistor may be rated in terms of its power dissipation. However, the cells should be operated well within their ratings in order to maintain repeatability of operation. It is important to operate photosensitive resistors well below their maximum voltage, if possible. This is because the device follows Ohm's law at fairly low voltages, while the resistance becomes a function of applied voltage at high levels. A point may be reached when the photosensitive resistor (photocell) breaks down under a high applied voltage, on the order of several hundred volts.

Although the photosensitive resistor has high temperature coefficients, these cannot be compensated because the temperature coefficient is a function of the incident-light intensity. It generally decreases as the light intensity increases. Circuits using these devices are either operated at high intensities or in an on–off mode so as to minimize this effect. Some photosensitive materials have lower temperature coefficients than others. Since the photosensitive resistor's temperature coefficient is usually designed around, self-heating due to internal power dissipation is allowable. This means that the photosensitive resistor can be used freely as a circuit element. The devices are given power ratings just like ordinary resistors. Some versions are available with heat sinks to increase the allowable power dissipation. These photoresistors may be used to control moderate loads, such as relay coils, without the necessity for intermediate amplification. The power-dissipation rating is intended for ambient temperatures of 25°C and below. Most manufacturers recommend that the rating be linearly decreased to zero at 75°C, since this corresponds to the maximum operating temperature.

The spectral sensitivity, or the "light frequency response," of the photoresistor is a function of the cell's material (see Fig. 2-5). Some materials have peaks in the red region, others in the blue region, while some are relatively flat over a wide range. The importance of the spectral sensitivity depends on the intended application. The spectral sensitivity and other characteristics, such as temperature coefficient, stability, and operating speed, are interdependent. Many different mixtures of photoconductive materials are utilized by manufacturers in order to fit specific applications.

The resistance of a photosensitive conductor does not change instantaneously with changes in light intensity. There is a time lag which may be on the order of milliseconds for common photoconductors. To make things still worse, the cell's resistance also depends on the past intensity. That is, the resistance of the cell at a given light intensity will depend on whether the cells was previously in the dark or exposed to a strong light source. This phenomenon is known as hysteresis or "light-history effect." While the magnitude of the light-history effect is not easily specified and measured, the speed of response is. The speed of response is different depending on whether the cell is going from light to dark or vice versa. Accordingly, the time required to go from dark to light (the rise time) is distinguished from the time required to go from light to dark (the fall time). This time is generally defined in either case as that required for a 63 per cent portion of the total resistance change. The rise time may be several times longer than the fall time. Both the rise and fall times decrease considerably with increased light intensities. High speed operation of these cells calls for the use of high light intensities as well as the most favorable materials.

PHOTOVOLTAIC CELLS

Unlike the photoconductive cell, which can be used only with an externally applied voltage, the photovoltaic cell can convert light to electricity directly. Alternatively, it may be used with an external voltage source as well. The materials most commonly used in the construction of the cells are germanium, silicon and selenium. The construction of a selenium cell shows three different layers (Fig. 2-6). The top layer, which is exposed to light, is a very thin metallic surface that is also transparent. The middle layer is composed of a thin coating of selenium. The interface between the first and second layers acts as a barrier between them. Below the second

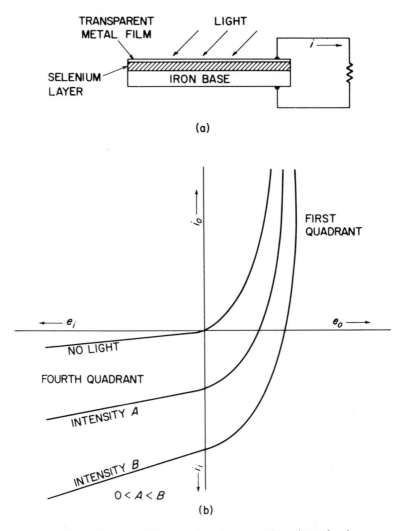

Fig. 2-6 Photovoltaic cell: (a) Cross-section view of selenium cell indicates selenium layer sandwiched between transparent metal film and iron baseplate. Direction of output current flow is shown. (b) The graph of four quadrant voltage-current characteristics as a function of applied light shows that the photovoltaic cell may either generate power (first quadrant) or act as a constant current load (third quadrant).

layer there is an iron base which serves both as an electrical connection and as a mechanical base. The other electrical connection is made to the transparent metal layer. When exposed to light, the top layer becomes negative with respect to the iron base. Because of the barrier, cells constructed in this way are known as *barrier cells.*

Cells constructed with silicon are made by a diffusion process. A very thin layer of N-type silicon is formed over a substrate of P-type silicon by the diffusion of the proper impurities. A P-N junction is formed. Connection is then made to both layers. The voltage–current characteristics of this device as a function of incident light may be plotted. Although the curves exist in the first, third, and fourth quadrants, the third and fourth quadrants are chiefly used. The fourth quadrant is the region where the cell looks like a battery. The cell is capable of delivering a current to a load. The greater the light intensity, the higher the open-circuit and the short-circuit current will be. The short-circuit current is a linear function of light intensity, while the open-circuit voltage increases logarithmically with light.

If a reverse bias is applied across the cell, its graph resembles that of a constant current source. This operation is confined to the third quadrant. The magnitude of the current source is a linear function of light intensity. Since an external voltage source is required for third-quadrant operation, the photovoltaic cell is clearly serving as a photosensitive resistor. There are several important differences between the back-biased photovoltaic cell and the cadmium sulfide or selenide photosensitive resistor. Among these are the greater linearity, faster response, and cell-to-cell uniformity of the photovoltaic cell.

If the photovoltaic cell has a large surface area, it may be useful in power generation. Such units are referred to as solar batteries because the sun is used as the light source. On the other hand, cells having very small surface area are known as photodiodes. If a second junction is added to a photodiode, a phototransistor results. The light intensity is equivalent to a base current. The advantage of small-area photodiodes and phototransistors is their fast response. In general, a large-area cell has considerable junction capacitances which limit frequency response. Cutting the cell area increases speed but limits the magnitude of the cell's output.

Temperature-Sensitive Resistors

The resistance of a conductor or semiconductor may vary with temperature (see Fig. 2-7). This resistance variation is usually nonlinear and may have a positive or a negative slope, or may show a combination of the two slopes across a temperature span. The term for the resistance of a thermally sensitive resistor may be approximated by the polynomial

$$R = R_o (1 + \alpha \, \Delta T + \beta \, \Delta T^2)$$

where R is the resistance at a given temperature, R_o is the resistance at T_o, and ΔT is the difference between T_o and the given temperature. The two constants α and β are known for a variety of materials; the value of β is usually too small to be significant in the value of R. The greater the value of

Fig. 2-7 (a) Thermistor construction. From left to right: washers, rods (3), discs (2), beads, and probes (photo courtesy of Fenwal Electronics, Inc.); (b—opposite) resistance sensor: The sensitivity of a thermistor compound and a platinum wire as a function of temperature. Note the small positive temperature coefficient of the platinum and the large negative coefficient of the thermistor.

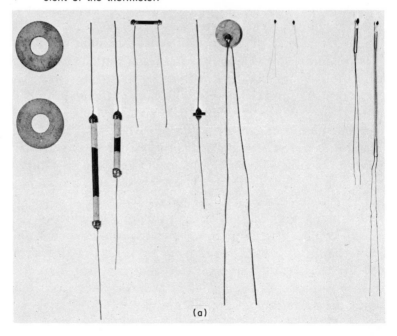

(a)

these constants, the more sensitive the resistor is to temperature changes. In the accompanying table there is a considerable difference in the magnitudes of the α constant. One group of materials, composed of pure metals and alloys, exhibits constants of orders of magnitude smaller than the second group, which is composed of semiconducting materials. The former group has a small temperature coefficient α. These materials are used to construct metallic-resistive temperature sensors. The latter group shows a much larger temperature coefficient. Temperature sensors using these materials are commonly known as *thermistors*. Although both types of sensor depend on the same basic property, the great differ-

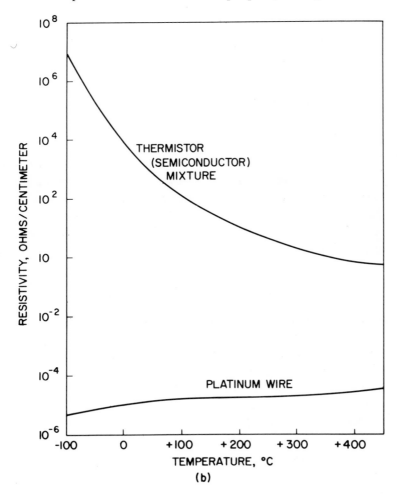

(b)

ence in temperature coefficient and end use warrants a separate discussion of each.

Resistance Temperature Coefficients for α
(per degree centigrade)

Aluminum	0.43%	Manganin	0.002%
Brass	0.20%	Nichrome	0.04%
Constantan	0.0002%	Nickel	0.68%
Copper	0.67%	Platinum	0.39%
Gold	0.40%	Silver	0.41%
Iron	0.61%	Tin	0.46%
Lead	0.39%		

Manganese oxide @	25°C	−4.4%
Manganese oxide @	100°C	−3.0%
Manganese oxide @	−25°C	−6.1%
Silicon		−4.0%

METALLIC-RESISTIVE TEMPERATURE SENSORS

Metallic-resistance temperature sensors are commonly made from wire which is rigidly supported and arranged so that the maximum amount of wire is fitted into the smallest desirable area. This insures that the bulk of the resistance variation with temperature is due to the sensor and not to the connecting wires and cables. A high-resistance sensor is preferred as the effect of the lead and contact resistances is minimized. The sensor is usually enclosed in a sealed case in order to provide electrical insulation and protection from contaminants. These contaminants can alter the properties of the wire if they form an alloy with it or otherwise change its composition. Occasionally, the resistance element is contained in an inert gas or solid. Because the sensitive element is not directly coupled to the ambient, there is a time lag between the change in ambient temperature and the corresponding change in sensor resistance. This time lag, or slowed response, must be accounted for in sensing systems.

The most commonly used metals include nickel, silver, gold, and platinum. Of these, platinum enjoys the widest use because it will not corrode and may be purchased in very high purities. For most temperatures the coefficient β can be ignored as it is quite small compared with α. The temperature of the sensor is the difference between the nominal resistance and the measured resistance, which is then divided by α. The nominal resistance R is specified for a temperature such as $0°C$ or $25°C$. Since the difference between the resistance and the nominal resistance may be quite small, a bridge circuit (Fig. 2-8a) is used for measurement. The output of the bridge is the potential difference between points A and B, or E_{ab}. A potential V is applied to points C and D. The resultant voltage at point A is

$$E_a = V\left(\frac{R_T}{R_T + 10R_o} \right)$$

The voltage at point B is

$$E_b = V\left(\frac{R_o}{R_o + 10R_o} \right)$$

Therefore,

$$E_{ab} = E_a - E_b$$

$$= V\left(\frac{R_T}{R_T + 10R_o} - \frac{R_o}{R_o + 10R_o} \right)$$

But

$$R_T = R_o + R_o(\alpha\, \Delta T)$$

Substituting,

$$E_{ab} = V\left[\frac{R_o + R_o(\alpha\, \Delta T)}{R_o + 10R_o + R_o(\alpha\, \Delta T)} - \frac{R_o}{11R_o} \right]$$

Since $R_o(\alpha\, \Delta T)$ is small with respect to $11R_o$, we may remove it from the denominator. Thus,

$$E_{ab} = V\left[\frac{R_o + R_o(\alpha\, \Delta T)}{11R_o} - \frac{R_o}{11R_o} \right]$$

$$= V\left[\frac{R_o(\alpha\, \Delta T)}{11R_o} \right]$$

$$= V\left(\frac{\alpha\, \Delta T}{11} \right)$$

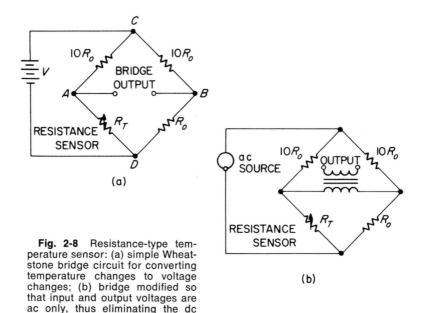

Fig. 2-8 Resistance-type temperature sensor: (a) simple Wheatstone bridge circuit for converting temperature changes to voltage changes; (b) bridge modified so that input and output voltages are ac only, thus eliminating the dc error due to thermoelectric effects.

The output voltage of the bridge is directly proportional to the temperature of the sensor. It is also a function of the voltage supply feeding the bridge. The magnitude of the bridge unbalance voltage may be quite small. Thermoelectric contact potentials caused by dissimilar metal junctions (to be discussed later) may cause a considerable error voltage. If the bridge is fed by an ac source (Fig. 2-8b), the thermoelectric error can be eliminated with ac coupling, as the thermoelectric term is dc only. If the current passed through the sensor is too large, enough power may be dissipated in the sensor to raise its own temperature.

THERMISTORS

A thermistor is a thermally sensitive resistor distinguished from other thermally sensitive resistors by its nonmetallic composition and large temperature coefficients. However, the large temperature coefficient is concommitant with unpredictable, imprecise operation.

Thermistors may be composed of sintered oxides of copper, iron, nickel, cobalt, and manganese.

The resistance of the negative temperature-coefficient thermistor decreases nonlinearly with increases in temperature. Although each unit has a nominal temperature coefficient, the manufacturer will generally supply curves of the thermistor resistance as a function of temperature. The resistance at 25°C is normally used as the nominal resistance value. (A sample resistance temperature plot is shown in Fig. 2-7.)

The resistance is solely a function of the thermistor temperature. There are several consequences of this. If the thermistor is used to measure a sense temperature then its resistance must be electrically monitored. If the monitoring circuits force a current through the thermistor it will dissipate power according to Power $= I^2 R$. The power so dissipated will raise the temperature of the thermistor. If the temperature rise in the thermistor due to the resistance sensing is significant it will cause sensing errors. Therefore the circuit which measures the thermistor resistance should cause a minimum power dissipation.

A second consequence is noted when the ambient temperature is suddenly changed. The thermistor tries to establish thermal equilibrium (the heat lost by the thermistor is equal to the heat gained) with the ambient. For example, if the ambient temperature dropped, the thermistor would have to give off heat to the ambient to re-establish equilibrium. This heat transfer cannot take place instantaneously as the thermal coupling between the thermistor and the environment is not perfect. Further, the heat transfer takes place exponentially, since the time constant is a function of the mass and the coupling to the ambient. Since the thermistor resistance is only a function of temperature, and the temperature of the device cannot change instantaneously, the resistance also cannot change instantaneously.

The voltage–current characteristics of the thermistor are

nonlinear. The reason for this is the internal temperature rise produced by the voltage–current products. At low power-dissipation levels the self-heat of the thermistor will not cause an appreciable change in resistance. At higher power dissipations the thermistor heats up. As its temperature increases the resistance goes down. Since power = (current)^{2}x (resistance), the power dissipation will also increase. This power-dissipation increase lowers the resistance still more. This condition lasts until the thermistor is drawing the maximum available power from the circuit. When maximum available power is drawn the thermistor is at its highest temperature. At this point the real part of the source impedance is equal to the thermistor resistance.

However, if enough heat is removed from the thermistor, it will not get hot enough to operate in the self-heating condition. The efficiency of heat conduction from the thermistor to the ambient will determine whether the operation will be in the self-heating mode.

The thermistor may be used in the same type of bridge circuit as the less sensitive metallic temperature sensor. Alternatively, it may be used in a simple voltage-divider network when large temperature changes are anticipated. In either event the thermistor is much more easily applicable to existing circuit parameters than the metallic sensor because it is available in a wide range of nominal resistances. As far as physical considerations, the thermistor also has an advantage because it may be had in a wide range of case sizes and configurations, while the metallic sensor is generally limited to rather large cylinders or flat plates. Despite these drawbacks, the metallic sensor is preferred in many instances because of its superior stability, linearity, and reproducibility. The thermistor cannot compete in these areas because the mixtures of which it is made cannot be controlled as closely.

THERMOCOUPLES

A thermocouple is a temperature sensor whose output is a voltage, not a resistance or capacitance change. The basic principle of the thermocouple is the thermoelectric effect, which was first observed in the early nineteenth century. If two wires of dissimilar materials are joined at both ends, and their joints, or junctions, are held at different temperatures, a current will flow in the circuit. If a break is made in the wires, not at a junction, a voltage may be measured. This voltage is a function of the two materials used and is closely proportional to the temperature difference between junctions. If the materials are known, and one junction is held at a known temperature, then the temperature at the other junction is readily found. The proportionality, or thermoelectric constant, is listed below in tabular form. Rather than list the constants for all possible combinations, each material is assumed to be used with platinum as the second metal. To find the constant for any two materials, the difference between the constants is used.

Thermoelectric Constants of Common Materials

(microvolts/°centigrade, platinum as the reference metal)

Bismuth	−72	Copper	6.5
Constantan	−35	Gold	6.5
Nickel	−15	Iron	18.5
Platinum	0.0	Nichrome	25
Mercury	0.6	Germanium	300
Carbon	3	Silicon	440
Aluminum	3.5	Tellurium	500
Lead	4	Selenium	900
Silver	6.5		

The magnitude of the thermoelectric voltage is normally quite small. The units for the thermoelectric constants are usually given in microvolts per degree centigrade. It can be seen that any system employing thermocouples has to be very sensitive. High-gain amplifiers must be employed to provide usable signal levels. Despite this disadvantage, the thermocouple is widely used as a temperature sensor. One reason for this is the high linearity of the transfer function. High order terms are not significant in the response. The second reason is the small size, simple construction, and ruggedness possible with these units.

The simplest thermocouple circuit is comprised of two dissimilar wires whose junctions are at T_1 and T_2 (Fig. 2-9a). When a measuring device is placed in the circuit, there will be three possible thermocouple junctions. If the measuring device is not composed of a material similar to one of the wires, the thermoelectric voltage will depend on the composition of all three materials as well as on the three junction temperatures. However, since a temperature sensor is most often used to measure the temperature at one point, the influence of two other temperatures is not desirable. The problem is ameliorated by keeping two junctions at a fixed, known temperature (Fig. 2-9b). Then the thermoelectric voltage for one junction simply indicates its temperature. The two secondary junctions are shown enclosed in dotted lines. This implies that they are kept in close proximity, as that is an easy method of keeping their temperatures equal. The two junctions are kept at the ambient temperature, which is usually room temperature. Although these junctions are by no means maintained at a constant temperature, corrections may be made to compensate for the temperature variation. The correction is generally done with a potentiometer moved by a bimetallic strip or with a thermistor in a bridge circuit. A small voltage of the proper polarity is added to the thermoelectric voltage. The amount of the voltage is proportional to the temperature difference between the reference junction and a standard temperature, such as 0°C or 25°C. Units of this type, known as thermocouple reference junctions, are manufactured for one or more thermocouples of commonly used thermocouple wires. Another method of maintaining the two secondary junctions at a known, fixed voltage is to keep them in an ice bath. This method affords good results, but is much less practical than the electronic reference junction (Fig. 2-9c).

Care must be taken in the measurement of the thermoelectric voltage. The current flow to the measuring device should be minimal because it contributes to errors in three ways. First, the current flow through the wires and junctions produces heating which tends to mask the temperatures to be measured. Also, a current flow tends to heat one junc-

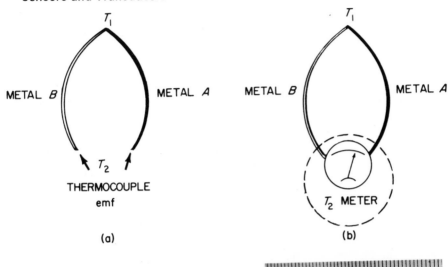

T_1

METAL *B*   METAL *A*   METAL *B*   METAL *A*

T_2

THERMOCOUPLE
emf

T_2 METER

(a)   (b)

Fig. 2-9 Thermocouple circuits: (a) The simplest thermocouple circuit has two junctions. (b) A thermocouple circuit with three junctions, two being held at the same temperature, is effectively a two junction circuit. (c) This thermocouple reference junction, known also as a cold junction compensator, obviates the need for two junctions being maintained at 0° C for calibrated measurements (photo courtesy of Consolidated Ohmic Devices, Inc.).

(c)

tion and cool the other. This is the inverse of the thermal voltage phenomenon. The third error is the voltage drop due to the circuit resistance. Although these errors can be minimized by using a physically large thermocouple, it is much easier to use a circuit which draws little current.

Resistive Humidity Sensors

In the measurement and control of humidity, resistive humidity sensors (e.g., sensors whose resistance is a function of the ambient humidity) are commonly applied. The electrical properties of these devices are in many ways similar to those of photosensitive conductors because both exhibit a large nonlinear change in resistance for relatively small input changes.

The sensor is usually constructed of a sensitive material which is deposited between two metallic conductors. Both the sensitive material and the conductors are mounted on a rigid form or substrate. The sensitive material is one whose conductance increases with increases in absorbed moisture. Metallic salts are commonly used. The conductors are arranged so that the area of contact is maximized. This lowers the magnitude of the sensor's resistance.

The construction of a typical cell is shown in Fig. 2-10. The cell may take considerable time to respond to a change in humidity. The response time will depend on such things as the presence of moving air, the ambient temperature, and the pressure. Response times in minutes may not be uncommon. The resistance of the cell at constant humidity is a function of temperature. This temperature sensitivity may be largely cancelled by using a reference cell with the meas-

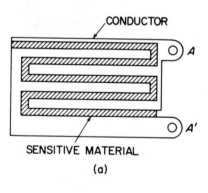

CONDUCTOR

SENSITIVE MATERIAL

(a)

Fig. 2-10 Resistive humidity sensor has a resistance which decreases with increasing humidity. Its disadvantage is slow response time and poor repeatability. (a) cross-section; (b) schematic symbol.

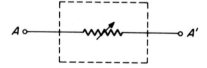

(b)

uring cell in a bridge circuit. The reference cell, which is sealed in a dry environment, is used to compensate for temperature changes only.

Because many cells use an electrolyte as the sensitive element, a dc voltage cannot be used to determine the cell resistance. A fairly low ac voltage is used instead. As with photoconductive cells, the peak applied voltage should be kept small to avoid cell breakdown.

EXPLOITING COMPONENT PROPERTIES
FOR SENSING

Every electronic component is sensitive to its environment to some extent. Since most components are used not as sensors but in applications which require stability regardless of the environment, a component's sensitivity is usually a defect. However, a small number of components which exhibit a sensitivity to their environment are known solely for their sensing applications. The distinction between an ordinary component and a sensor is somewhat arbitrary in many instances. The fact that a device or component that is not commonly known as a sensor may make an excellent one is, unfortunately, usually overlooked. With some imagination one can find usable sensing qualities in a large number of devices. The result is that the designer can increase the number of devices at his disposal which may work, resulting in possible economies of cost and design.

For example, transistors are widely used, but they are hardly ever used for sensing. Yet the transistor's sensitivity to ambient temperature is well known. There are many transistor parameters which are temperature dependent, but the most useful parameter is V_{be}. The base-to-emitter voltage of a transistor is a linear function of temperature, and its derivative with respect to temperature is fairly constant for all types of transistors (see Fig. 2-11).

The slope of the base–emitter voltage is nearly the same for both germanium and silicon transistors. However, the break-voltage (the voltage necessary for forward bias) differences for the two types are evident in the characteristics.

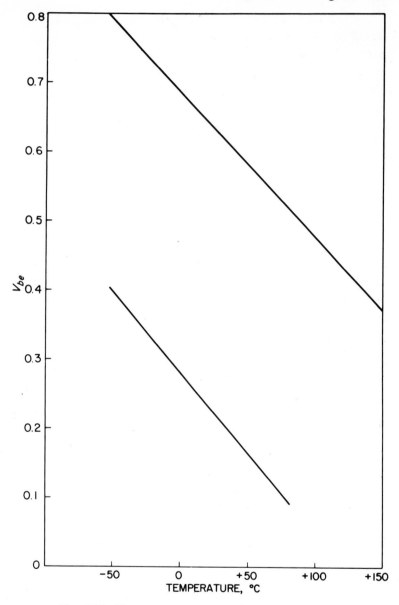

Fig. 2-11 The graph of transistor base-emitter voltage as a function of temperature shows linear relationship. Upper curve is silicon transistor; lower curve is germanium.

The application of the base–emitter characteristics may take advantage of the transistor's ability to amplify currents.

The transistor may be used as a combination amplifier–sensor (Fig. 2-12a). The case of the transistor is coupled to the ambient temperature by conduction. When the transistor's base–emitter junction is colder than the temperature needed to make V_{be} equal to V_{input}, then the base–emitter junction will be reverse biased, and no appreciable collector current will flow. When the temperature of the junction increases so that V_{input} is equal to the break voltage, the simplified equivalent circuit (Fig. 2-12b) is valid. Analysis of the equivalent circuit shows that the transistor will be in the active region for a small range of temperature (Fig. 2-12c). When the base current is equal to $(V_{cc}/R_L)/h_{fe}$, then the transistor will be saturated. No further change will occur for any further increase in temperature. This simple circuit acts very much like a thermostat, but it has no moving parts.

Some precautions should be taken to ensure proper operation of this circuit. First, the source impedance of V_{input} should be low so that the transistor's reverse leakage current, I_{cbo}, will not influence the magnitude of the base voltage. Second, the collector load resistor R_L should be made as large as possible so that the transistor's power dissipation while in the active region will be small. If the transistor must dissipate too much heat, the self-heating effects will mask changes in the ambient temperature. The maximum operating temperature for the transistor temperature sensor is approximately 125°C.

The same sensitivity to temperature is found in many other semiconductors. The voltage across a germanium or silicon diode is temperature sensitive in the same manner as the V_{be} of germanium or silicon transistors. Strings of series-connected diodes may be used for a greater sensitivity. For example, if five silicon diodes are connected in series, the voltage drop at 25°C will be approximately three volts and dV/dT (rate of voltage change per degree) will be five times as much as the dV/dT of a single diode (10 mv/°C).

Semiconductors such as silicon-controlled switches and unijunction transistors, which are latching (or negative-resistance) devices, are found to exhibit a linear dependence between firing voltage and temperature. A circuit similar to

Fig. 2-12 Transistor temperature sensitivity used in sensing circuit: (a) schematic diagram; (b) schematic redrawn with transistor replaced by equivalent circuit; (c) voltage output as a function of temperature.

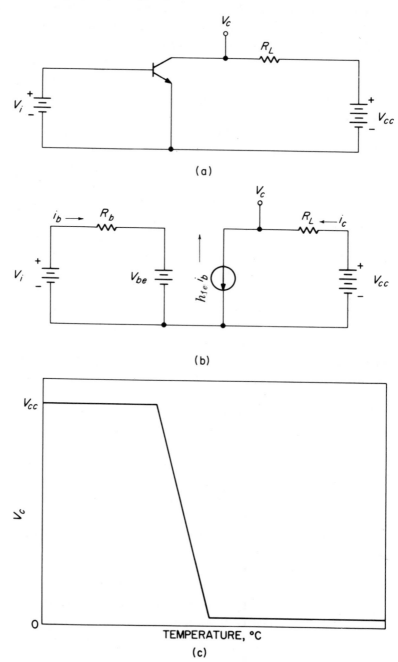

that of Fig. 2-12a may be used to exploit these characteristics.

The types of components usable as sensors are not limited
to active devices. Although thermally sensitive resistors
(thermistors) have long been used as sensors, thermally sensitive capacitors have found little application.

We have given several examples of how ordinary components may be used as temperature sensors. It is usually easy
to find devices which make good temperature sensors when
the thermal characteristics are given. One should not be
discouraged from looking for other types of sensors because
of the lack of published data. Simple experiments are often
useful in determining the existence of sensing properties.
For example, by exposing the base–emitter junction of a
transistor to light, perhaps through a protective lens, one may
find that the effect of the light is the same as a base current
would produce, and thus that the transistor may serve as a
sensitive photosensor.

3

Electronic Circuitry

The electronic circuitry required to convert the sensor's output to a command or datum may take many different forms, depending on the sensor, the required performance, and the available components. Therefore any discussion of electronic circuitry for controls must not dwell on any specific circuit, but rather should describe families of circuits. The circuits to be described here were selected because of their wide use in electronic sensing controls. Both discrete semiconductor and integrated-circuit implementations will be used.

Basic circuit properties of semiconductors will be reviewed in this chapter in order to acquaint or refresh the reader with the operation of diodes and transistors. These devices will be analyzed through reduction to simple equivalent circuits. Basic circuitry using integrated circuits will also be discussed using transfer functions and equivalent circuits. After this review we will be able to study a number of very useful control circuits, such as the Schmitt trigger, comparators, and operational amplifier circuits. Since the general approach to control design is more important than specific applications, the qualitative operation of the circuits will be stressed.

REVIEW OF DIODES AND TRANSISTORS

The semiconductor diode (see Fig. 3-1) acts as a unidirectional gate for current. It is characterized by a forward and reverse orientation. When the diode's anode is more positive than its cathode it is in the forward direction. An ideal diode has zero resistance, and hence no voltage drop due to current. When the cathode is more positive than the anode, the diode is reverse biased. An ideal diode has infinite resistance in this mode. However, actual semiconductor diodes exhibit a nonlinear resistance when forward-biased and a leakage current in the reverse direction.

A first approximation of semiconductor diode operation is

$$i = I_o \left(e^{v/\eta vT} - 1 \right)$$

where I_o is the diode reverse saturation current, v is the voltage across the diode (positive with respect to the anode), and vT is 26 millivolts at room temperature and $\eta = 2$.

When v/vT is negative, the exponential is small compared to one. This is the reverse-biased state, and the diode current is then approximately I_o. Since I_o does not change appreciably with changes in reverse voltage, we may term it a saturation current. This current will generally increase with an increase in temperature. The reverse saturation currents for silicon diodes are usually of orders of magnitude smaller than for germanium diodes.

When v/vT is positive the diode is forward-biased. The exponential term will now be large compared to one. If the diode's voltage–current characteristics are plotted on a linear scale the first quadrant (forward-biased) curve will show

Fig. 3-1 Schematic symbol for semiconductor diode.

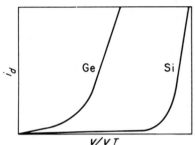

Fig. 3-2 Graph of v/vT versus i_d for germanium and silicon diodes.

two slopes. The first slope, from $v = 0$ to $v = V_{ci}$, is slight, indicating only a slight increase in current for an increase in voltage. However, when v is greater than V_{ci}, the current increases rapidly for an increase in voltage. The voltage at which the diode passes current easily is called the cut-in voltage, V_{ci}, or the diode voltage, V_d. Figure 3-2 shows a plot for silicon and germanium diodes. The cut-in voltage for the germanium diode is lower than the cut-in voltage for the silicon diode. However, the curve for the silicon diode has a much sharper break. This is caused by the constant $1/2$ which appears in the exponent (v/vT) of the above equation for silicon, and by a much lower I_o. These factors prevent reasonable currents until the v/vT term is fairly large. Hence the larger cut-in voltage.

Because it is unnecessarily difficult to analyze diode circuits with the diode equation, we will approximate the characteristics with an equivalent circuit. This equivalent, Fig. 3-3, consists of an ideal diode in series with a battery and a resistor. When forward-biased the ideal diode has zero resistance, so the circuit looks like a battery in series with

Fig. 3-3 Diode equivalent circuit in forward-biased operation.

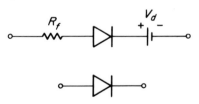

a resistor. The battery supplies a voltage equal to the diode
voltage V_d, and thus subtracts V_d from the applied voltage.
The resistor simulates the drop across the diode caused by
an increase in current. It is called the diode forward resistance, R_f. When the diode is reverse-biased the ideal diode
looks like an open circuit.

A reverse bias cannot be increased without limit. At a certain reverse voltage the current will start to increase rapidly.
This phenomenon, which is called breakdown, normally
causes destruction of the diode. The diodes are usually operated so that the breakdown voltage is never approached.
However, certain diodes, known as breakdown, avalanche,
or Zener diodes, are designed to operate in the breakdown
region without being damaged. The forward characteristics
of these diodes are similar to ordinary diodes. The reverse
characteristics show a sharp increase in diode current when

Fig. 3-4 Forward and reverse characteristics of a semiconductor diode (expanded scale).

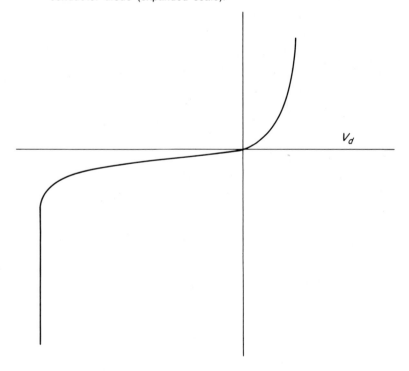

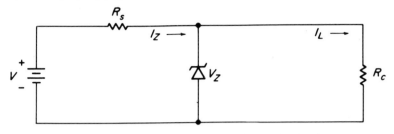

Fig. 3-5 Zener diode voltage regulator circuit. Current through R_s is constant, and Zener diode current is the difference between the current through R_s and load current.

a certain reverse voltage is exceeded. This voltage is known as the Zener voltage. The voltage across the diode stays constant over a wide range of currents (see Fig. 3-4). These properties are very useful, and two applications will be discussed.

In power supplies one often desires a constant output voltage with changes in load current. If the Zener diode is used as a regulator (Fig. 3-5) it is able to maintain a constant voltage across itself. Note that the diode is in the reverse direction. If the output current is zero and the output voltage is V_Z, then $I_Z = (V - V_Z)/R_s$. When no load current is drawn the power dissipation in the Zener diode is a maximum, as it carries the most current. Thus, with a given Zener voltage, supply voltage, and power dissipation, the series resistor R_s is specified. Also, there must be sufficient current through the diode to maintain it in the breakdown region. With the diode's maximum and minimum currents fixed, the variation in the load current is also fixed, because the sum of the diode current and the load current is always constant (assuming supply and output voltage is constant).

Transistor Circuitry

The bipolar transistor may be represented by a simple equivalent circuit consisting of a resistor, a diode, and a current source. This equivalent circuit is not the most exact representation, and it is not valid for high frequencies, but it will serve our purpose. The circuit in Fig. 3-6 is for NPN

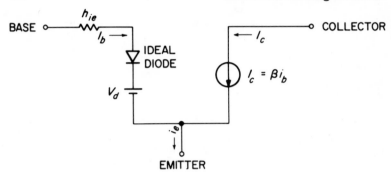

Fig. 3-6 Transistor equivalent circuit.

transistors. The circuit is valid for the NPN's complement, the PNP, when the direction of the diode, the current source, and the voltage source are reversed. The magnitude of the current source is a constant multiple of the base current i_b. We will assume that this constant is the same both for small signal variations in i_b and for large changes as well.

The equivalent circuit for small-signal operation (ac) does not require the input diode (Fig. 3-7). The constant of proportionality is β (Beta). We may also note that the emitter current is the sum of the base and collector currents.

When the transistor is used as a circuit element, one of its three terminals may be selected as a common or reference point. Depending on which terminal is chosen, the circuit may have many different properties. We will discuss the circuit properties of the common-emitter and common-collector configurations. The common-base circuit is little used in sensing controls and will not be treated.

Fig. 3-7 Transistor small-signal equivalent circuit.

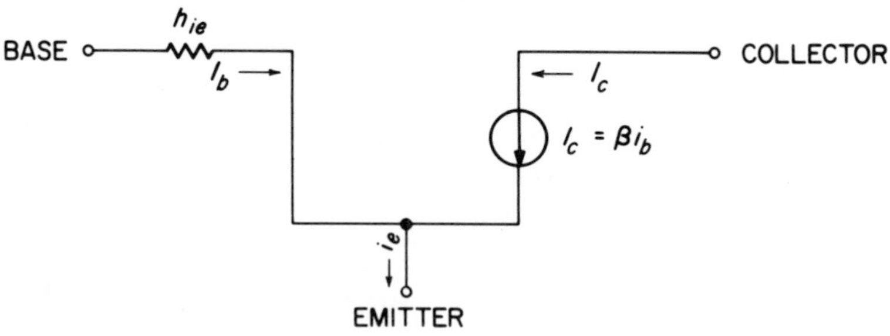

BASE o——h_{ie}—————————o COLLECTOR
i_b →   ← i_c

$i_c = \beta i_b$

i_e

EMITTER

The small-signal model will be used to derive the input impedance, output impedance, and voltage gain of each circuit (see Fig. 3-8). The results will also hold for dc operation when the static voltage drops are accounted for. The results are valid only where the models and equivalent circuits are valid—at less than one-tenth of the device's cut-off frequency.

THE COMMON – EMITTER CONNECTION

The common-emitter stage in its most general form may have an impedance connected from the emitter to ground (Fig. 3-9). For analysis we will find the properties of this stage when this is either zero or larger.

From the equivalent circuit replacement with $R_e = 0$ we see that the input impedance is merely h_{ie}, which is in the vicinity of 1000 ohms for many transistors. The output impedance is found by first assuming a constant value of open-circuit output voltage. When a resistive load can cut the output in half, the value of the resistor is the output impedance. The common-emitter output voltage is the product of the collector current and the load impedance. Thus, the output voltage is proportional to the load impedance. To get the output voltage to drop by one-half we must halve the load impedance, or parallel the load resistor with an equal resistance. This means that the output impedance of the common-emitter stage is the impedance from the collector

Fig. 3-8 Transistor small-signal equivalent circuit used to derive input and output impedance and voltage gain.

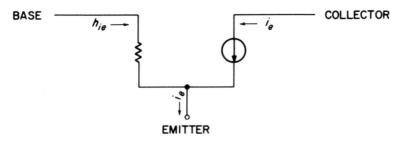

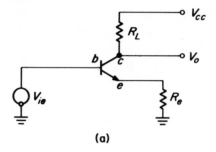

(a)

Fig. 3-9 (a) Common emitter connection; (b) common emitter connection redrawn with small-signal equivalent circuit $R_e = 0$.

(b)

terminal to the signal ground (which may also be the supply voltage).

To calculate the voltage gain of the common-emitter stage with no emitter impedance we first assume an input voltage, V_i. Then we calculate the output voltage and divide by the input voltage.

Applying a base voltage V_i, we produce a base current $i_b = V_i/h_{ie}$. Further, $i_c = \beta i_b$. But the output voltage is the product of the collector current times the collector load impedance.

Thus,

$$V_o = i_c R_L = \beta i_b R_L = \frac{\beta V_i R_L}{h_{ie}}$$

Thus

$$A = \frac{V_o}{V_i} = \frac{\beta R_L}{h_{ie}}$$

The properties of the common-emitter stage change considerably when there is an emitter impedance. As we see from the preceding equations, the properties of the common-emitter stage without an emitter impedance follow very closely the properties of the transistor. However, this is undesirable for two reasons. The transistor's parameters will change greatly over a temperature range. Also, there is a considerable variation of parameters from unit to unit. A circuit such as this may work for one transistor but not for another. It would be very desirable for a circuit's properties to depend on component values rather than on transistor parameters. We approach this ideal when an impedance is added to the emitter lead.

The modified circuit and its equivalent are shown in Fig. 3-10.

We calculate the input impedance as before. Calling the voltage at the emitter terminal V_e,

$$i_b = \frac{V_i - V_e}{h_{ie}} \quad \text{and} \quad V_e = i_e R_e$$

But

$$i_e = i_c + i_b$$

Fig. 3-10 (a) Common emitter configuration for a transistor amplifier stage; (b) circuit in (a) redrawn with transistor replaced by equivalent circuit.

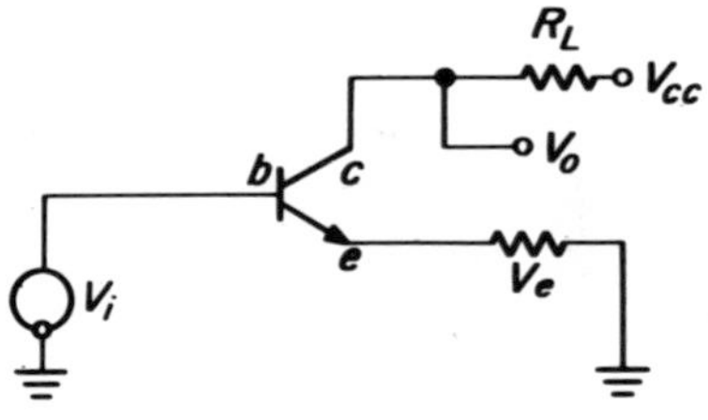

(a)

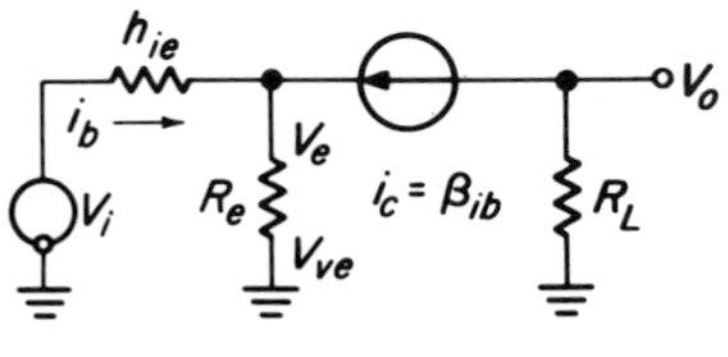

(b)

Therefore,

$$i_b = \frac{V_i - i_e R_e}{h_{ie}}$$

$$= \frac{V_i - R_e i_c - R_e i_b}{h_{ie}}$$

$$= \frac{V_i - R_e (\beta + 1) i_b}{h_{ie}}$$

Rearranging,

$$i_b \left[1 + \frac{R_e}{h_{ie}} (\beta + 1) \right] = \frac{V_i}{h_{ie}}$$

But the input impedance is V_i/i_b, or

$$Z_i = h_{ie} \left[1 + \frac{R_e}{h_{ie}} (\beta + 1) \right] = h_{ie} + R_e (\beta + 1)$$

Performing the calculation for the output impedance, we find that it is still equal to the impedance between the collector and signal ground.

To calculate the gain we assume an input signal V_i. The input current i_b is equal to V_i/Z_i, or

$$i_b = \frac{V_i}{h_{ie} + R_e (\beta + 1)}$$

The output voltage $V_o = i_c R_L$. But

$$i_c = \beta i_b = \frac{\beta V_i}{h_{ie} + R_e (\beta + 1)}$$

Therefore,

$$V_o = R_L i_c = \frac{\beta R_L V_i}{h_{ie} + R_e (\beta + 1)}$$

The gain

$$A = \frac{V_o}{V_i} = \frac{\beta R_L}{h_{ie} + R_e (\beta + 1)}$$

If $R_e (\beta + 1) \gg h_{ie}$, then

$$A = \frac{\beta R_L}{R_e (\beta + 1)}$$

Further, if $\beta \gg 1$ (the usual case), then

$$A = \frac{R_L}{R_e}$$

Thus the gain is now primarily a function of the ratio of R_L and R_e. The two inequalities will usually hold true for most circuits.

We summarize the properties of the common-emitter stage as follows. The configuration with no emitter resistance has a low input impedance, a high output impedance, and a high voltage gain. As the emitter resistance is increased, the input impedance increases and the gain is lowered but is more predictable.

One important application of the common-emitter circuit is the transistor switch (see Fig. 3-11). A conventional switch may be either open or closed. The open switch passes no current, while the current passed by the closed switch depends only on the external circuit. The transistor switch

Fig. 3-11 Transistor switch: (a) applying power with a switch; (b) the switch replaced with a transistor.

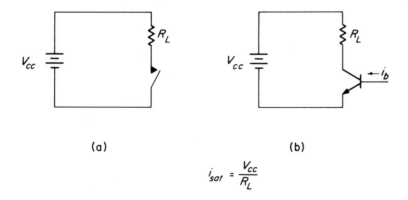

(a)   (b)

$$i_{sat} = \frac{V_{cc}}{R_L}$$

also has two states. When the base current, and therefore the collector current, is zero, the transistor is cut off. This corresponds to an open switch. When the maximum current, which is circuit-determined, flows, the transistor is saturated.

The saturation current is V_{cc}/R_L. The base current required to reach saturation is i_{sat}/β. One imperfection of the transistor switch is the fact that the load resistance is not grounded. There is a small voltage present between collector and emitter regardless of how much excess base current (beyond the saturation value) flows. This voltage is called the collector-emitter saturation voltage ($V_{ce\text{-}sat}$). This voltage is usually lower than V_{be}.

The power gain of the transistor switch may be considerable. For example, suppose that we had a transistor with $\beta = 100$, a maximum collector current of 1 ampere, and a maximum collector voltage of 50 volts. The transistor could then control 1 ampere at 50 volts, or 50 watts. The necessary base current would be 0.01 ampere and the base to emitter voltage approximately 0.7 volt. Therefore the input power, or controlling power, is 70 milliwatts. The power gain is the ratio of the load power to the controlling power, or about

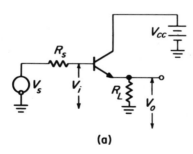

(a)

Fig. 3-12 Common-collector connection: (a) common-collector circuit; (b) circuit redrawn with small-signal transistor equivalent.

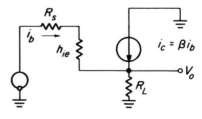

(b)

700. Although the transistor switches 50 watts, it need only be rated for 1 watt. When the transistor is on, the drop across it is low. When the transistor is off, very little current flows. The net power that the transistor must dissipate is therefore also low.

THE COMMON-COLLECTOR
CONNECTION

The common-collector connection is shown (see Fig. 3-12). We shall derive some of its useful properties and show how it complements the common-emitter stage.

To calculate the input impedance we find the base current due to an input voltage and divide the latter by the former. The base current

$$i_b = \frac{V_i - V_e}{R_s + h_{ie}}$$

$$V_o = V_e = i_e R_e = i_b R_e (\beta + 1)$$

$$i_b = \frac{V_i - i_b R_e (\beta + 1)}{R_s + h_{ie}}$$

$$i_b \left[1 + \frac{R_e (\beta + 1)}{R_s + h_{ie}} \right] = \frac{V_i}{R_s + h_{ie}}$$

Z_i is equal to V_i/i_b, or

$$\frac{V_i}{i_b} = [R_s + h_{ie}] \left[1 + \frac{R_e (\beta + 1)}{R_s + h_{ie}} \right]$$

$$= R_s + h_{ie} + R_e (\beta + 1)$$

To calculate the output impedance we add enough load impedance to cut the output voltage in half. A constant input voltage is assumed. With no load, the output voltage is equal to the input voltage, V_{in}. The output voltage V_o is equal to $i_e R_L$.

$$i_e = (\beta + 1) i_b$$

$$V_o = R_L (\beta + 1) i_b$$

But
$$i_b = \frac{V_i}{Z_i}$$

$$= \frac{V_i}{h_{ie} + R_s + R_L(\beta + 1)}$$

Therefore,

$$V_o = \frac{R_L(\beta + 1) V_i}{h_{ie} + R_s + R_L(\beta + 1)}$$

R_L is equal to the output impedance when $V_o = \frac{1}{2}V_i$, or

$$\frac{1}{2} = \frac{R_L(\beta + 1)}{h_{ie} + R_s + R_L(\beta + 1)}$$

Solving for R_L,

$$R_L = \frac{h_{ie} + R_s}{\beta + 1}$$

Thus,

$$Z_o = \frac{h_{ie} + R_s}{\beta + 1} = R_L$$

The voltage gain of the common-collector stage is very close to, but less than, unity. Since the output voltage of the stage closely follows the input voltage, this type of circuit is often called a *follower*. The follower is used for transforming impedances from high to low. The voltage gain of the transistor is fed back to cause this transformation. Thus, the emitter-follower is a current amplifier.

The input and output impedances of the common collector, or follower, were derived above from the small-signal transistor model. These results are also true for direct current, except that then the emitter voltage always differs from the base voltage by a diode voltage drop. The emitter-follower can be used in this way to shift the dc level of a waveform without altering the ac component. This is not analagous to capacitor coupling, as the response extends to direct current. Shifts in voltage greater than a diode drop can be made by inserting a fixed voltage drop between the emitter terminal and the emitter resistance. This fixed voltage drop may be produced with a diode, a Zener diode, or even a battery. So long as the voltage source has a low dynamic impedance, the derived relations for the emitter-follower will hold.

The emitter-follower is an extremely useful circuit to use as an input, output, or interstage coupling. When used as an input circuit it presents a high impedance. This minimizes loading effects. As an output circuit it presents a low output impedance. Thus the load will not greatly affect waveform or amplitude of the output. The ratio of impedance transformation of the emitter-follower is proportional to β. However, the β-values available may not be high enough to meet certain applications. For these applications a cascade of emitter-followers, known as a Darlington configuration, is often used. The emitter current of the first transistor is the base current of the second transistor. The emitter current of the second transistor is approximately its β-value times its base current. Thus, the emitter current of the second transistor is approximately the product of the β-values of both units times the input base current.

The two transistors of the Darlington configuration may be replaced with a single transistor whose β-value is the product of the individual β-values. Compared to the emitter-follower, the Darlington stage has a higher input impedance and a lower output impedance, assuming transistors with equal β in both circuits. Since the output is separated from the input by two base-emitter drops, the input voltage will always be $2V_d$ greater than the output voltage at direct current.

THE SCHMITT TRIGGER

The Schmitt trigger is a bistable circuit whose state is a function of the input voltage. The transfer function shows four points of transition (Fig. 3-13). As long as the input voltage is less than V_1, the output voltage will remain in the zero state. If the input voltage is greater than V_2, the output

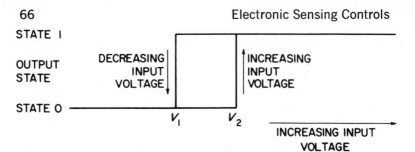

Fig. 3-13 Transfer function of Schmitt trigger shows two states and four switching points. The switching point from state to state depends on the state of the circuit before switching. The difference between the switching points is the *hysteresis voltage.*

voltage will remain in the one state. When the input voltage is between V_1 and V_2, the output may be either state. If the input voltage was originally lower than V_1, and it became greater than V_1 but less than V_2, the output remains zero. Similarly, if the input voltage was originally greater than V_2, the output would remain one until the input voltage fell below V_1. The vertical lines represent transitions and are not stable states.

Thus the Schmitt trigger exhibits a different action depending on whether the input is increasing or decreasing. The circuit tends to favor the state that it is in. It may only take a small increase above a nominal value for the circuit to change state, while a much larger decrease below this nominal value is required to change state again. This property is known as *hysteresis.* The difference between the switching points, V_1 and V_2, is referred to as the *hysteresis voltage.*

The Schmitt trigger is widely used in sensing controls because it converts quantitative information (how much light, heat, moisture, etc.) into qualitative information (yes or no, sufficient, insufficient). The qualitative information is converted into a voltage to drive the circuit's input. The output may control a relay, or a silicon-controlled rectifier, or any other electrically controllable device. Because of hysteresis the circuit is less likely to respond to electrical noise and transients.

The term "Schmitt trigger" was originally applied to

cathode-coupled or emitter-coupled bistable multivibrators. However, the term has come to apply to any circuit with the same type of transfer function. The transfer function is generally performed by an amplifier with both positive feedback and a loop gain greater than unity. The transfer function of a Schmitt trigger as a function of loop gain is shown in Fig. 3-14. With a loop gain of less than unity there is no sharp transition between states. Indeed, there is an infinity of stable states. When the loop gain is exactly one, only two stable states exist. However, there is no hysteresis voltage. The hysteresis voltage requires a loop gain greater than unity. Generally, the more loop gain a circuit has, the more rapidly its transition will take place.

A given circuit may have several important characteristics and parameters. These may include the input impedance, switching voltage, hysteresis voltage, the speed of response,

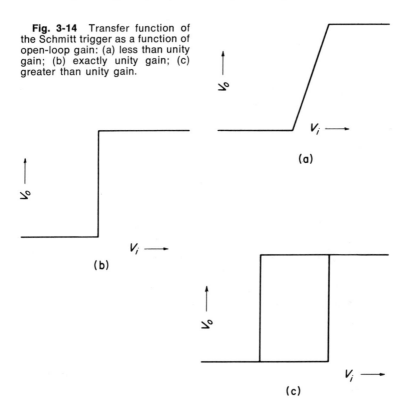

Fig. 3-14 Transfer function of the Schmitt trigger as a function of open-loop gain: (a) less than unity gain; (b) exactly unity gain; (c) greater than unity gain.

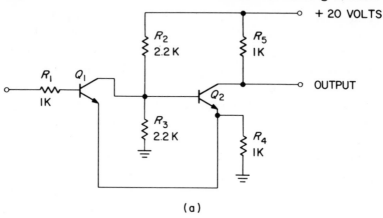

(a)

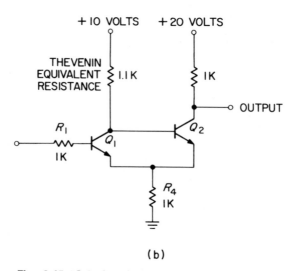

(b)

Fig. 3-15 Schmitt trigger: (a) two-transistor circuit; (b) circuit redrawn and simplified; (c—opposite) equivalent circuit when Q_1 is on and Q_2 is off; (d) equivalent circuit when Q_2 is on and Q_1 is off; (e) transfer function of Schmitt trigger.

and the temperature stability. A high input impedance may be important when the input source cannot deliver much current. A low input impedance might cause errors due to loading. The switching voltage should be flexible enough so that it may be set for the most favorable input voltage range. It should be stable and free from drift so that frequent adjustments are unnecessary. Hysteresis should provide a

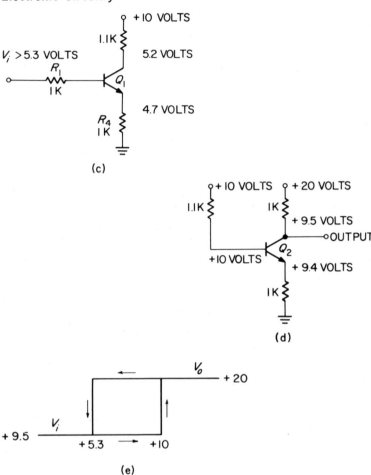

(c)

(d)

(e)

voltage band of sufficient width to prevent false triggering. Response time of the circuit should be small so that there is no unwarranted time delay between input and output.

TYPICAL CIRCUITRY

A representative Schmitt trigger using two NPN transistors is shown in Fig. 3-15a. The transistors have their emitters tied together. Also, the collector of Q_1 is connected to the base of Q_2. Since the drop between the emitter and collector of Q_1 (when Q_1 is saturated) is normally much lower than the voltage needed to maintain the base-to-emitter junction of Q_2 in the active region, Q_2 will be cut off when Q_1 is saturated. Due to the current supplied through R_2, Q_2 will be on when Q_1 is off. The configuration of Q_1 and Q_2 is inherently bistable. Positive feedback arises from the common-emitter return through R_4. In order to limit the amount of base current forced through Q_1, R_1 is interposed.

For analysis we may replace R_2 and R_3 by the Thevinin equivalent, as in Fig. 3-15b. Further, we can assume very high betas, a collector-to-emitter saturation voltage of 0.1 volt, and an active or saturated base-to-emitter drop of 0.6 volt. These values imply the use of good-quality silicon transistors. When Q_1 is saturated, Q_2 will be off. Therefore the current flowing through R_4 is solely due to Q_1. This same current flows through the Thevinin equivalent load resistance. Redrawing the circuit eliminating Q_2, the voltage across R_4 is seen to be 4.7 volts (Fig. 3-15c). To maintain this state requires that Q_1 be active or saturated, or that the drop between base and emitter be 0.6 volt. Thus, the input voltage must be greater than 4.7 + 0.6 volt, or 5.3 volts, to be in this state. When Q_2 is off, there is no current flow through R_5, so the output is constant at 20 volts.

If the input voltage falls below 5.3 volts, Q_1 will come out of saturation. Its collector–emitter voltage will rise until it is sufficient to turn on the base–emitter junction of Q_2. Current starts to flow out of the emitter, increasing the drop across R_4. This increase tends to turn off Q_1 still further. This transition is regenerative, and once initiated it proceeds with great speed. Finally Q_1 is cut off and the circuit may be redrawn with Q_1 omitted (Fig. 3-15d). Because of the large β there is virtually no drop across the Thevinin equivalent load resistance. Therefore, the voltage at the base of Q_2 is 10 volts. The emitter voltage is 0.6 volt lower, or 9.4 volts. The collector is at a level 0.1 volt higher than the emitter, or at 9.5 volts. The output state is accompanied by a current flow through R_5. It can be seen that the output will not change state until Q_2 is turned off. This requires that Q_1 enter the active region almost to the point of saturation. Since both emitters are biased at 9.4 volts, the base of Q_1 must rise above $0.6 + 9.4$, or 10 volts, before transition occurs.

The graph of the transfer function given in Fig. 3-15e shows the two switching points of the circuit. The hysteresis is fairly large, 4.7 volts, with respect to the mean switching voltage. Although this Schmitt trigger is very simple it has a number of disadvantages. The switching and hysteresis voltages are dependent to a moderate degree on the supply voltage as well as on the temperature. Further, the input impedance varies widely, depending on whether Q_1 is cut off, lightly saturated, or heavily saturated.

A scheme to greatly increase the input impedance of this Schmitt trigger is shown in Fig. 3-16. A PNP emitter-follower stage precedes Q_1 and provides an impedance transformation.

The Comparator

As its name implies, the comparator circuit compares the magnitude of two input voltages. The output is usually binary, i.e., it has only two states. For a pair of input terminals A and B, there will be an output state corresponding to $A > B$ and a state for $A < B$. When both input voltages are very close in value $(A = B)$ the output may sometimes be ambiguous. For most applications this region of ambiguity is undesirable. Generally, the smaller the region of am-

Fig. 3-16 Emitter follower (common-collector stage) added to input of Schmitt trigger to increase input impedance.

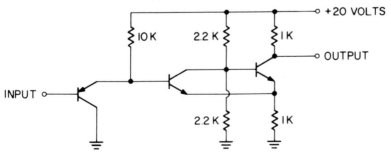

biguity, the more precise the comparison. For example, if a comparison between two 1-volt signals, with 1 per cent precision, is desired, then the maximum permissible ambiguity is 0.01 volt. A commonly used term for this ambiguity is *resolution*. Resolution is an important parameter for it determines how close to ideal the circuit really is. Another important quality of the comparator is its speed of response. This is a measure of how soon the state actually changes when the input conditions warrant a change in state. Sometimes a rapid response is desired, but occasionally it is not important. For example, consider the use of a comparator to convert an unknown voltage to a digital number, which occurs in digital-readout voltmeters. The unknown voltage is connected to one input terminal. A very linear, stable voltage ramp is applied to the other terminal. The slope of this ramp in volts per second is known. When the ramp voltage exceeds the unknown input voltage the comparator changes state. Since the ramp's initial voltage and slope are known, the time of coincidence determines the value of the unknown voltage. Here the response must be rapid, as any delay in changing state makes the unknown voltage appear higher in magnitude than it really is. On the other hand one can find many applications where the speed of response is of little consequence. A comparator used to sense the amount of light incident on a cadmium-sulfide or cadmium-selenide photocell need not be much faster than the photocell response. This may be measured in milliseconds. It may be advantageous to slow down the response of a comparator in this type of situation, since it will then be less sensitive to electrical transients and noise.

The applications in which a comparator may be used are similar to the applications of the Schmitt trigger. We may list the similarities and differences between the circuits. Both circuits function with quantitative, analog inputs and produce binary, qualitative outputs. The Schmitt trigger has a single input terminal and supplies its own reference to determine the switching points. It has a true binary output; there are no ambiguous states. The comparator is inherently a differential device, for its state depends only on the difference between its two terminals. It has an ambiguous output region. However, it is a much more versatile circuit than the Schmitt trigger. A Schmitt trigger may be made

Fig. 3-17 (a) Simple differential comparator circuit and (b) transfer function.

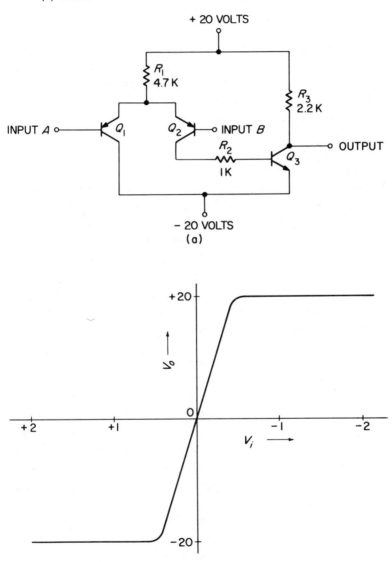

with a comparator but the converse is not true. Since the advent of integrated-circuit comparators, many circuit functions which were formerly performed by Schmitt triggers have been done by comparators.

IMPLEMENTATION

A conventional, low-resolution comparator uses three transistors (Fig. 3-17). For analysis assume that input B is grounded. For Q_2 to be on there must be a base–emitter drop of 0.6 volt. Thus, the emitter of Q_2 is at $+0.6$ volt when it is on. Collector current flows through R_2 and the base–emitter junction of Q_3, turning it on when Q_2 is also on .The output is then clamped to approximately -20 volts. If the voltage at input A rises above zero, the base–emitter junction of Q_1 will begin to be reverse-biased. The most negative voltage at either terminal determines the voltage of the common emitters. Therefore, if the voltage at terminal A decreases, the common-emitter voltages also go down. Since input terminal B is clamped to ground, the base–emitter junction of Q_2 is reverse-biased when the voltage at terminal A decreases. The collector current flow ceases, and Q_3 is cut off. The output voltage rises to $+20$ volts. Between these two output states there is a region of ambiguity of perhaps a tenth of a volt, referred to the input.

The comparator is a true differential device. Which input has the signal to be compared or the standard of comparison do not matter. The only difference between the two inputs is the phase relationship between the input and the output. If input B is held fixed and input A rises, the output tends to decrease. If input A is held fixed and input B rises, the output will also tend to rise. Therefore, a change at input A will tend to produce an opposite-polarity change at the output. A change at input B tends to produce an output change which is in phase, or in the same direction as the input change. Since a voltage at input A produces an inverse change at the output, input A is called the inverting, or negative, terminal. Input B is called the noninverting, or positive, terminal. The electronic symbol for a comparator is a triangle with two inputs at the base and an output at the apex (Fig. 3-18a). The noninverting and inverting inputs are marked with a plus sign and a minus sign respectively.

The region of ambiguity in the comparator's transfer function is most interesting. Not only does a small input difference produce a large output, but the slope of the input–output curve is fairly linear (see Fig. 3-18b). This implies that if the two input voltages were fairly close, the circuit would function as an amplifier. The gain of the amplifier would be proportional to the slope of the curve. Indeed, this same circuit configuration is known as a differential pair, and is widely used in the design of differential amplifiers. A differential amplifier is defined as an amplifier whose output is a constant multiplied by the difference between two input voltages. This constant is generally called the open-loop gain, since negative feedback is often used to reduce the net gain. Thus the circuit can be used either as a comparator or as a differential amplifier. The difference between a circuit used as a comparator and one used as a differential amplifier is that certain parameters are emphasized for each. The output voltage swing in a comparator does not have to be large, only large enough to be useful. The input terminals should be usable over a wide voltage range without damaging the circuit. A fast response is usually desirable.

COMPARATOR APPLICATIONS

The most obvious use of comparators in electronic sensing controls is for comparison between physical phenomena. Any physical phenomenon which can be converted to electrical form by a sensor or transducer may then be compared with either the output of another similar transducer or with a reference. For example, suppose one wanted to know when the temperature at one point equalled the temperature at another point. This could be accomplished by placing a thermistor at both points and generating a voltage propor-

Electronic Sensing Controls

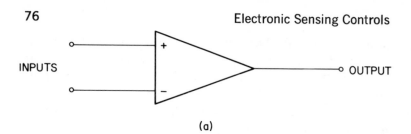

(a)

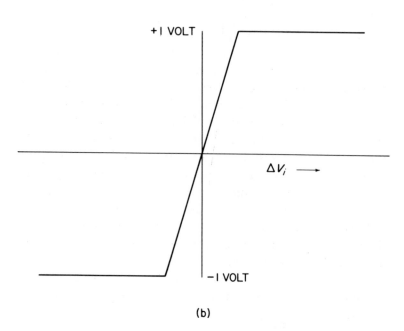

+ I VOLT

$\Delta V_i \longrightarrow$

− I VOLT

(b)

Fig. 3-18 (a) Comparator symbol; (b) typical comparator transfer function (c—opposite) Schmitt trigger implemented with a comparator; (d) resultant transfer function showing the effect of positive voltage feedback.

tional to temperature with a resistor-divider network. The voltages corresponding to the temperature at each point would be fed to the comparator to indicate coincidence. If one only wanted to know when a certain temperature at a point was exceeded, only one thermistor voltage divider would be used. Assuming that the temperature-to-voltage characteristics of the divider were known, the divider voltage could then be compared to a potentiometer voltage.

A simple system for determining when two displacements

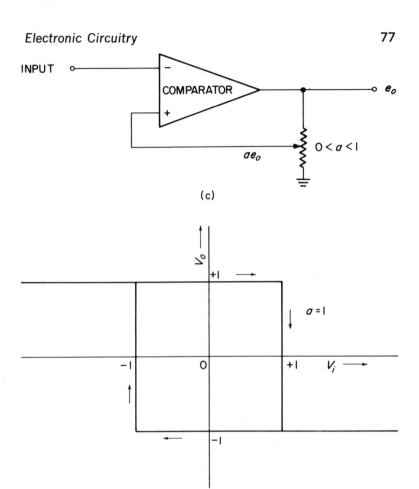

(c)

(d)

are equal is shown in Fig. 3-19. The two potentiometers R_1 and R_2 are linear potentiometers whose slider position is a function of linear displacement, not rotation. Twenty volts are applied across the entire winding of both potentiometers. The slider voltage can then vary from +10 volts to −10 volts, depending on the displacement of the slider arm. The comparator output will then be determined by the difference of displacement between both slider arms.

The comparator circuit can also be used to make a Schmitt trigger. The comparator's transfer function and the schematic are shown in Figs. 3-18b and c. The two output states

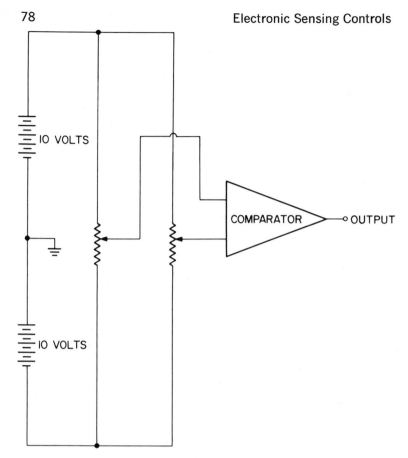

Fig. 3-19   Comparator circuit for determining when two displacements are equal.

are +1 volt and −1 volt. The voltage fed back to the positive terminal is a fraction a of the output voltage, where a may vary from zero to one. The output voltage is determined by $E_o = A\,(-E^- + E^+)$, where E^- is the voltage at the negative terminal, and E^+ is the voltage at the positive terminal, and A is the open-loop gain. For analysis assume that $a = 1$ and the input voltage is −2 volts. E_o is then positive, but it can only reach +1 volt. Therefore E^+ is also +1 volt. The voltage at the negative input must rise to +1 volt before the comparator changes state. When +1 volt is exceeded, the output changes to −1 volt. In this state the input must fall to −1 volt to change the state.

When $a = 1$, the hysteresis voltage is equal to the peak-to-peak output voltage, which is two volts. The hysteresis voltage may be decreased to zero by changing a. The Schmitt trigger's closed-loop gain is the product of A, the open-loop gain, and a, the potentiometer constant. When this product is equal to one, the hysteresis voltage will be zero. When the product is less than one, the circuit will function as a comparator only. The effect of the positive feedback through the potentiometer will raise the slope (equivalent to increasing the gain) of the transfer function.

The transfer function for this comparator implementation of the Schmitt trigger is similar to that shown for the conventional Schmitt trigger except that the curve is rotated about the output voltage axis (see Fig. 3-19b). This is due to the inversion of the input voltage by the use of the inverting input terminal. The situation is analagous to first inverting the input voltage and then feeding it to a conventional Schmitt trigger.

The Differential Amplifier

The differential amplifier is an unusually versatile and powerful circuit which is widely used in electronic sensing controls (see Fig. 3-20). The advent of inexpensive integrated-circuit differential amplifiers will further increase its use. Basically, a differential amplifier produces an output which is proportional to the voltage difference between its input terminals. The quotient of proportionality is known as the gain. The circuit is useful in three main areas. First, it is invaluable in the amplification of extremely low-level

Fig. 3-20 Differential amplifier symbol and governing equation.

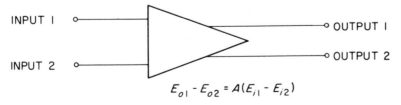

INPUT 1

INPUT 2

OUTPUT 1

OUTPUT 2

$$E_{o1} - E_{o2} = A(E_{i1} - E_{i2})$$

signals which may have large unwanted signals, such as hum and pickup, combined with them. So long as the unwanted signals are common to both inputs, the differential amplifier will reject the unwanted and amplify the desired signals. Since the output of certain transducers may be below a millivolt, this property is very important. The second area of application is the use of the amplifier in feedback configurations. Since both inverting and noninverting terminals are available, negative or positive feedback is quite easy to apply. The net gain and the frequency response can be determined simply and accurately. Since the open-loop gain without feedback is usually quite high, the performance of the amplifier is solely a function of the feedback network. The third use of the amplifier is for operational circuits, where the amplifier is used primarily for its tremendous gain. Differential amplifiers for operational use may have gains from one thousand to several million. These large gains make the amplifier unusable without some form of feedback. Operational amplifier circuits were first used in electronic analog computers, where they performed the functions of addition, subtraction, differentiation, and integration. As the amplifier gained popularity, it began to supplant other types of circuits because of the ease with which it could be applied.

The basic differential-amplifier circuit is the differential pair (Fig. 3-21). The amplifier uses two transistors for gain, and a third, Q_3, as a constant-current sink for the emitter currents of the two gain transistors. The output may be taken off in differential form or single-ended. For differential output, both load resistors are used, while the single-ended output may be taken from either load resistor. The gain for a differential output is twice the gain for a single-ended output because one output swings downward by the same amount as the other swings upward. By using both the downward as well as the upward swing the net output change for a given input change is twice that obtained by using a single-ended output. The gain for a stage such as this may be on the order of one or two hundred. A high-gain differential amplifier may have a cascade of two or

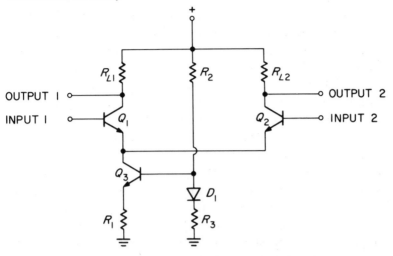

Fig. 3-21 Circuit implementation of a differential amplifier shows "differential pair," Q_1 and Q_2, as well as constant current source Q_3. Because this circuit is symmetrical, it will operate the same way when both the input and the output terminals are interchanged.

more differential pairs, followed by an emitter-follower to lower output impedance. Gains of more than ten thousand may be realized in this fashion.

Aside from the gain, there are many other parameters of interest for a differential amplifier. Some of these include the frequency response, the offset voltage and current, the common-mode rejection ratio, and the maximum peak-to-peak output voltage swing. These terms will be discussed separately.

"Frequency response" is a measure of how the gain of the circuit varies with frequency. Generally, the differential amplifier has direct coupling throughout. There are no capacitors to limit the gain at dc, so the gain at dc will be maximum. As the frequency increases, the effects of the transistor's interelement capacitances become evident and result in a decrease in gain. This decrease in gain asymptotically approaches an integer multiple of 6 db per octave, or 20 db per decade of frequency. If the gain of the amplifier equals one when the rate of gain decrease is 12 db per octave or greater, then the differential amplifier will be unsuitable for any use which requires the application of negative feedback. The reason for this is beyond the scope of this book; however, if this occurs, the negative feedback will become positive feedback and will cause oscillations. For this reason, differential amplifiers are sometimes compensated so that this condition does not exist. The frequency at which the gain of the amplifier is unity is referred to as the gain bandwidth of the amplifier. The higher the gain bandwidth, the higher the frequency of possible use. If the amplifier is used with a feedback network to limit the gain, the open-loop gain (the gain without feedback) should be more than ten times higher than the closed-loop gain (the gain with feedback) at the highest frequency of interest. Wide frequency response and high gains do not usually go hand in hand, and one is often sacrificed to improve the other.

Offset voltage and current are error terms. An ideal differential amplifier may be thought of as following the equation $E_o = E_1 - E_2$. If $E_1 - E_2$ is zero, then the output should be zero. This is not realized in practice. Actual circuits have an output when there should be none. A portion of this output is present if the input terminals are shorted. Another portion of the output is proportional to the resistance between each input and ground. The first part of the error voltage is called the offset voltage because it is independent of the resistance between the input terminals and ground. Since the magnitude of the remaining term is proportional to the input resistances, it is known as the offset current. These terms, which are visible only at the amplifier's output, are commonly divided by the open-loop gain so as to refer them to the input of the amplifier. Their effect appears as an error term in the operation of the circuitry. These offset terms exist because of mismatches in the transistors and resistors. Although they are temperature dependent, these terms can often be minimized. If the resistance between the input and ground is made the same for both the positive and negative inputs, only the difference in offset currents is amplified. The offset current which is common to both terminals produces equal voltages at the inputs, which is then rejected as being a common-mode signal. The offset voltage can often be nulled or cancelled by applying a small trimming voltage to the input. Many other schemes are also used to reduce these effects.

The common-mode rejection ratio is a measure of how well the differential amplifier rejects signals which appear simultaneously at both input terminals. If both input terminals of an ideal differential amplifier were tied together, the output would always remain zero, no matter what voltage was applied to the inputs. However, an actual amplifier would respond to common-mode signals. The ratio between the common-mode signal applied to the input and the resultant change at the output, which is expressed in decibels, is called the common-mode rejection ratio. For example, if

Fig. 3-22 (a) Operational amplifier in inverting configuration and governing equation. (b) Operational amplifier used to take the inverse of the sum of the input voltages. The values of the resistors determine the weighting given to each input according to the equation.

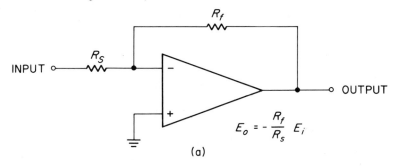

$$E_o = - \frac{R_f}{R_s} E_i$$

(a)

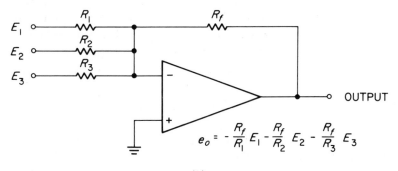

$$e_o = - \frac{R_f}{R_1} E_1 - \frac{R_f}{R_2} E_2 - \frac{R_f}{R_3} E_3$$

(b)

both input terminals of a differential amplifier were tied together and applied to a one-volt source, the output might rise one microvolt. This corresponds to a 120 db common-mode rejection ratio. The minimum usable figure for most applications is at least 60 db. Below this figure the differential properties of the amplifier are questionable. Another similar parameter is the supply-voltage rejection ratio which is a measure of how a change in supply voltage affects the output voltage.

The peak-to-peak output voltage of a differential amplifier is generally specified by graphical methods. It may be a function of output load resistance as well as of frequency. It does not usually correspond with the gain vs. frequency characteristics. The open-loop gain of an amplifier can be at the maximum while the maximum output has decreased considerably. A well designed amplifier may be capable of an output swing at dc which is almost as great as the supply voltages.

The differential amplifier obeys the equation $E_o = A (E^+ - E^-)$, where E^+ and E^- are the voltages at the positive and negative terminals, and A is the open-loop gain.

Operational – Amplifier Circuits

An operational amplifier is a high gain differential amplifier with high input impedance and low output impedance. Its gain is usually so high that it must be used with some form of negative feedback. This is often advantageous, as the resultant characteristics are very stable and predictable. One of the most common configurations is the inverting amplifier (Fig. 3-22a). For the analysis of this and other operational-amplifier circuits employing feedback the assumption is commonly made that the voltage between the input terminals is zero. This is valid because it only takes a small voltage at the inputs to produce a very large output voltage, assuming linear operation. The feedback will always keep the interterminal voltage very small, just large enough to produce the required output voltage. For the inverting amplifier, the signal voltage E_i is applied to the negative terminal through resistance R_s. Since the positive terminal is grounded, the negative terminal must sit very close to ground. This means that the effect of the output voltage, which is applied to the negative terminal through R_f, when added to the effect of the input voltage, must produce zero volts at the input. Mathematically,

$$\frac{E_i R_f}{R_f + R_s} + \frac{E_o R_s}{R_f + R_s} = 0 \qquad \text{or} \qquad E_i R_f = -E_o R_s$$

$$\text{or} \qquad E_o = -\frac{E_i R_f}{R_s}$$

This result may be arrived at by other means. When the positive terminal is grounded, the negative terminal sits very close to ground because of negative feedback. The impedance from the negative terminal to ground is generally quite high. Since the voltage to ground at this point is virtually zero, we may assume that almost no current flows into the negative input. This is equivalent to saying that the current which flows in toward the negative input is balanced by an equal and opposite current, supplied through the feedback path. Because the negative input is so nearly a ground, it is called a virtual ground. In reality, a high impedance separates this point from ground. Because the currents flowing toward this point are summed to produce a null, it is also called a summing junction. For example, suppose that there were three input resistors, R_1, R_2, and R_3, and three input voltage sources, E_1, E_2, and E_3, as in Fig. 3-22b. The current flow toward the virtual ground would be

$$\frac{E_1}{R_1} + \frac{E_2}{R_2} + \frac{E_3}{R_3}$$

An output voltage E_o would be produced so as to bring the negative terminal to ground. This output voltage, when applied through R_f, would produce an equal and opposite current. In other words,

$$\frac{E_o}{R_f} = \frac{E_1}{R_1} + \frac{E_2}{R_2} + \frac{E_3}{R_3}$$

Rearranging,

$$E_o = R_f \left(\frac{E_1}{R_1} + \frac{E_2}{R_2} + \frac{E_3}{R_3} \right)$$

By selecting appropriate resistance ratios this configuration can be used for adding or subtracting with any multiplier. If an inversion, or sign change, is needed, this circuit may be used with equal-valued resistors for R_1 and R_f.

The basic inverting-amplifier circuit of Fig. 3-22a may be easily converted to an ideal integrator or differentiator. By

Fig. 3-23 (a) Operational amplifier connected as an integrator. (b) Operational amplifier connected as a differentiator.

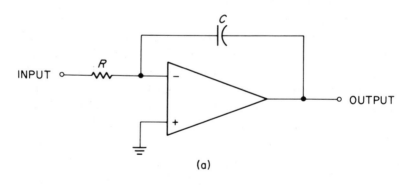

(a)

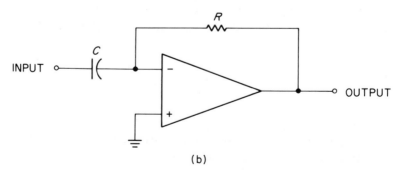

(b)

replacing either R_f or R_s by a capacitor, an integrator or a differentiator is created. In the integrator of Fig. 3-23a, the capacitor is placed between the output and the negative input. To analyze, we assume that the current flowing through the capacitor is equal and opposite to the current in the resistor. That is, $E_i/R_s = -I_c$, where I_c is the current through the capacitor. But $I_c = C (dV/dt)$, the product of the capacitance and the rate of change of the voltage across the capacitor. Since one end of the capacitor is connected to a virtual ground, the voltage across the capacitor is equal to the output voltage. Replacing V by E_o, we have

$$I_c = C\left(\frac{dE_o}{dt} \right) = \frac{-E_i}{R_s}$$

Solving for dE_o,

$$dE_o = \frac{E_i dt}{R_s C}$$

This result is in differential form. When integrated from $t = 0$ to $t = T$ we get the resultant

$$E_o = \frac{1}{R_s C} \int_0^T E_i dt + V$$

where V is the voltage on the capacitor at time $t = 0$. Thus it is seen that the input voltage is integrated and multiplied by a constant to produce the output voltage. This circuit, known as a Miller integrator, has many uses. It may generate a linear ramp in response to a constant input voltage. Or it may be used in the simulation of an integrator for an electronic analog computer.

The differentiator (Fig. 3-23b) is the twin of the integrator circuit. In this circuit the capacitor is connected between the signal input and the negative terminal. As in the integrator, the current through the capacitor is equal and opposite to the current flowing through the resistor. The current through the resistor is E_o/R_f. The current in the capacitor, I_c, is equal to $(dE_i/dt)/C$. Multiplying the capacitor current by -1 and equating,

$$\frac{E_o}{R_f} = C \left(\frac{dE_i}{dt} \right)$$

Solving for E_o,

$$E_o = R_f C \left(\frac{dE_i}{dt} \right)$$

In other words, the output is the time derivative of the input, multiplied by a constant. The differentiator may be used in the same types of applications as the integrator. However, since a differentiator's gain increases with fre-

Fig. 3-24 (a) Operational amplifier in noninverting amplifier configuration; (b) Operational amplifier used as a voltage follower.

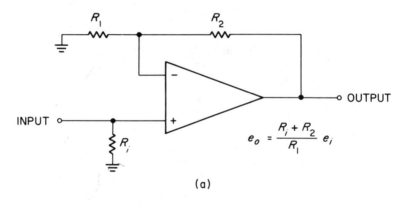

$$e_o = \frac{R_i + R_2}{R_1} e_i$$

(a)

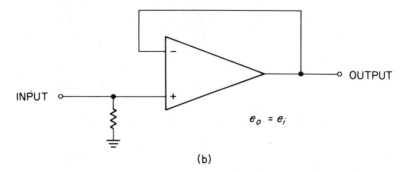

$$e_o = e_i$$

(b)

quency, it is inherently susceptible to high frequency noise and spurious transients.

The second most common configuration for operational amplifiers (Fig. 3-24a) provides for the signal to be fed directly to the positive terminal. Negative feedback is applied through R_1 and R_2. Since the gain of the amplifier is so high, the signal present on the positive terminal is also present at the negative terminal, through negative feedback. The output signal which is divided by the R_1 and R_2 voltage divider is the signal which appears at the negative terminal. Mathematically,

$$E_i = \frac{E_o R_1}{R_1 + R_2}$$

Solving for the gain,

$$\frac{E_o}{E_i} = \frac{R_1 + R_2}{R_1}$$

If R_1 were equal to R_2, the gain of the stage would be two. If these same constants were used in an inverting configuration the gain would be -1. Note that the gain for the circuit where the input is applied to the positive terminal is always positive, or noninverting. For this reason this configuration is sometimes known as the noninverting configuration.

We can see that as R_1 becomes much larger than R_2, the gain of the circuit will approach one. In the limit, R_1 becomes infinite and R_2 becomes zero (Fig. 3-24b). This circuit, which has a gain of exactly one, is the operational-amplifier follower, or buffer. This circuit does not give a voltage gain, but effects an impedance transformation, or current gain, from input to output. For this reason it is often used to prevent loading without introducing large voltage drops, as the transistor emitter-follower would do. It is important to remember that this circuit, as well as all other operational-amplifier circuits, requires a dc path to ground from both input terminals so that the input offset and bias currents have a return.

THE MONOSTABLE MULTIVIBRATOR CIRCUIT

The monostable multivibrator circuit is used for the generation of pulses and time delays. Although there are many other types of circuits which perform the same task, the monostable multivibrator, or "one shot," is the most representative and the most widely used. As the name implies, the circuit is a multivibrator with one stable state. Upon the application of a trigger pulse the circuit changes to an unstable state, in which it remains for a fixed length of time. Then it returns to the stable state once more. A simple one-shot circuit is shown in Fig. 3-25a. In the quiescent state Q_1 will be off and Q_2 will be on. The base current required to keep Q_2 on is supplied through R_4. The collector of Q_2 sits at $+0.1$ volt due to the saturation. Similarly, the base of Q_2 is clamped to $+0.6$ volt because of the drop between base and emitter. Since Q_1 is off, no collector current is drawn, and the collector sits at $+5$ volts. The capacitor is charged to $+4.4$ volts from the collector of Q_1 to the base of Q_2.

A narrow positive pulse is applied to the input of the circuit to turn Q_1 on. The collector voltage falls very rapidly from $+5$ volts to $+0.1$ volt, corresponding to a drop of

Fig. 3-25 (a) Monostable multivibrator circuit showing quiescent voltages; (b—opposite) input waveform for a typical timing cycle; (c) output waveform; (d) base waveform.

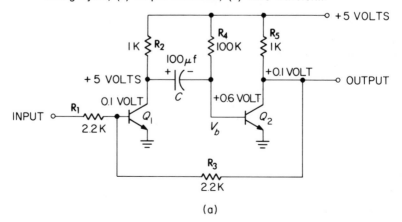

(a)

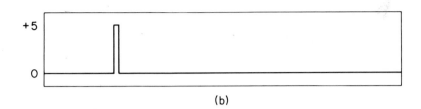

(b)

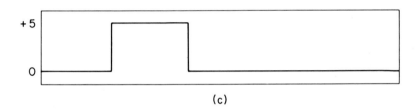

(c)

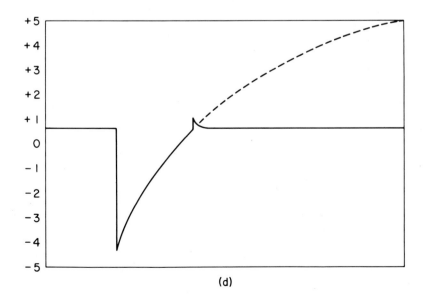

(d)

4.9 volts. Since the voltage across the capacitor cannot change instantaneously, the 4.9-volt drop is transmitted directly to the base of Q_2. This puts the base at $0.6 - 4.9$ or -4.3 volts, cutting Q_2 off. The collector voltage rises and maintains Q_1 on because of the current supplied through R_3. Meanwhile the negative end of the capacitor starts to charge toward the $+5$-volt supply through R_4. However, it will never reach $+5$ volts because Q_2 will turn on when the negative end reaches 0.6 volt, enough to turn on Q_2. The time required for this is easily calculated. The initial capacitor voltage is $+4.9$ volts. If the negative end were to reach $+5$ volts while the positive end remained at $+0.1$ volt, the final capacitor voltage would be -4.9 volts. The voltage across the capacitor is given generally by the equation $V_c = A + B \, (\exp -t/RC)$,* where A and B are constants, V_c is the capacitor voltage, t is in seconds, and RC is the product of R_4 and C. At the time of transition $t = 0$, so that the initial capacitor voltage is A, or $+4.9$ volts. When t goes to infinity, the capacitor voltage reached (theoretically) is -4.9 volts. Thus, $A + B = -4.9$ and $A = +4.9$. Therefore, $B = -9.8$ volts. The equation which describes the voltage on the capacitor is then $V_c = +4.9 - 9.8 \, (\exp -t/RC)$. When the base voltage rises to $+0.6$ volt, V_c is -0.5 volt, and the circuit changes state. The equation for the time in the unstable state simply sets the capacitor voltage equal to -0.5. Thus

$$-0.5 = 4.9 - 9.8 \, \exp \left(\frac{-t}{RC} \right)$$

$$\frac{-5.4}{-9.8} = \exp \frac{-t}{RC} = 0.55$$

$$\exp \frac{t}{RC} = \frac{1}{0.55} = 1.82$$

$$\frac{t}{RC} = \log_e 1.82 = 0.6$$

$$t = 0.6 \, RC$$

---

*The notation exp ( ) is often used in place of e( ) in literature; $\exp(-t/RC)$ and $e^{-t/RC}$ are synonymous.

With the values shown the output pulse width will be approximately 6 seconds.

The monostable multivibrator is generally used to stretch or lengthen the output of sensors in order to operate devices which require considerable operating time. For example, if a slow-acting relay or solenoid is to be operated from the output of a photocell whose pulse width may be very small, a monostable multivibrator or similar time delay must be interposed. The circuit may also be used to create delays between an input transition and an output transition.

4

Photoelectric Controls

A photoelectric control is operated by the presence, absence, quality, or quantity of light. Similar controls may be operated by invisible electromagnetic radiation, such as ultraviolet, infrared, or radio waves, or X rays. It is rare that the quantity to be controlled is light itself. Rather, the control of objects interposed between the light source and the sensing control is more commonly desired. An object may interrupt a light beam without physical contact, and at a distance. There is no inertia in a light beam. The speed of a photoelectric control is determined by the control only.

Photoelectric controls have many disadvantages. Light from the sun or other lighting may impinge upon the sensor and mask the absence of light from the desired light source. Dust or dirt may come between the light source and the light sensor and stop the light flow. The light beam may be visible to the eye.

The basic photoelectric control (Fig. 4-1) is composed of a light source and a light sensor. An object, when interposed between the two, will change the amount of light incident upon the sensor. The change in light is detected and used to actuate the control. Alternatively, an object may normally

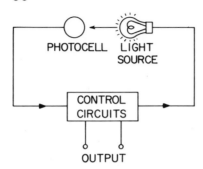

PHOTOCELL LIGHT
           SOURCE

CONTROL
CIRCUITS

OUTPUT

Fig. 4-1 Basic photoelectric control consists of light source, photocell, and control circuitry.

be interposed between the light source and the sensor. The control will operate on removal of the object. *or photo cell in*

The most commonly used sensors include phototubes, light-sensitive photoconductors, photovoltaic cells, photodiodes, and phototransistors. Phototube controls will not be discussed here because they have been largely supplanted by other devices. Likewise, vacuum-tube circuits are now little used; they have been replaced by solid-state and integrated circuitry. The most popular sensor is the photosensitive resistor.

The basic photoelectric control is primarily used for the detection of objects. There are many different ways that the control may operate, depending on the object. The light source may be separate from the light sensor, or it may be in the same package. The necessary electronics may be mounted with the sensor, or it may be separate. Lenses and prisms may or may not be used for transmission and reception of the light beam.

The simplest approach consists of a separate light source and sensor. The light source and the sensor are separated so that there is enough room for an object to intervene. When the sensor and the source are too far apart the control may not operate for two reasons. The intensity of light from a point source decreases with the square of the distance from the source. Thus an interruption of the light is less pronounced. Also, stray light from lighting, sunlight, etc., will mask the effect. Therefore, placing a large distance between source and sensor requires a high intensity and discrimination from uncontrolled light sources.

High intensity is usually achieved with a lens system. A proper lens system will focus the light into a beam of parallel rays whose intensity will not decrease considerably with distance. When these rays arrive at the sensor, the intensity can be further increased by another lens system to focus the parallel rays directly upon the most sensitive area of the sensor. Discrimination between the light source and unwanted light is most simply achieved by mounting a long tube (Fig. 4-2) over the sensor. This cuts out light from all directions except the axis. The longer the tube, the more stray light will be eliminated. If the tube is too long, the control may be difficult to aim.

Two other methods for adding discrimination are the use of polarizing filters and the use of a modulated signal. "Polarization of light" refers to the orientation of the light wave. A light beam may be vertically polarized, horizontally polarized, or a combination of the two. Certain film filters have the property of passing light of one polarization more

Fig. 4-2 Long tube may be used to shut out extraneous light, so that only desired light source will operate control.

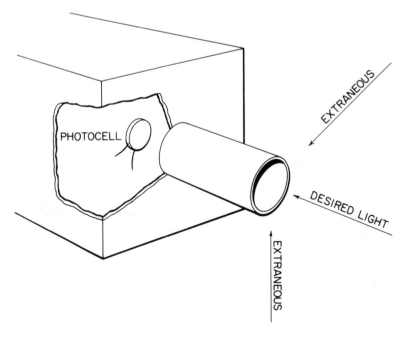

easily than light of another. If such a filter is used both at
the light source and at the sensor, the control will respond
preferentially to light from the sensor. As the glare from
reflected sunlight usually has a predominantly horizontal
polarization, a vertically polarized light source and sensor
will reject the glare. The other method is the use of a modulated light beam. The modulation, which is a change in light
intensity, may be square wave (on–off) or sine wave. The
varying light wave will produce a varying voltage at the
output of the sensor. Most unwanted light has little variation, so a simple capacitor can be used to block its effect.
A number of light sources which are operated by ac turn on
at each half cycle. These include fluorescent lighting and
neon bulbs. Therefore, a modulated light system should not
use the ac frequency as the modulation signal, and should
discriminate between the ac frequency and the modulation
frequency.

One of the disadvantages of using a separate sensor and
light source is that the two units must be aimed at each
other. This means that the source, the interrupting object,
and the sensor must be in one line. The more efficient the
system, the more focusing it has. This makes aiming difficult.
Further, once the units are aimed, they must maintain their
alignment for the proper operation of the control. Many
mechanical schemes have been used to aid aiming. They
include swivel brackets, ball joints, etc. As the distance between the sensor and the source is increased, the aiming task
becomes more difficult.

Although the electronics can be housed with the sensor,
the most common packaging for this type of control consists of separate sensor, source, and electronic-circuitry pack-
ages. The sensor and the source are connected to the circuitry
by cables which can be armored for protection. Keeping the
sensor and the source apart from the circuitry allows the
latter to be large in size and easily accessible for operation,
adjustment, and servicing. There are two reasons why the
light source is powered by the circuitry rather than being
powered directly. The easiest beam to focus is produced by
a small filament which requires low voltages and high cur-

rents. This is most conveniently supplied by a transformer. Since the circuitry is transformer-operated too, both windings can be combined on the same transformer. The wires from the circuitry to the light source carry low voltage and do not present a shock hazard. However, low resistance wiring must be used to prevent excessive voltage drop.

The use of a separate light source and sensor is certainly the simplest and most direct way to construct a photoelectric system. However, there are applications where it would be desirable to have only one unit which combines the necessary functions. Photoelectric controls which combine a light source and sensor in one package are called reflex controls. Aside from the physical advantages, aiming a reflex control is much simpler than aiming a two-part control because the light source and sensor are already aligned with each other.

One representative reflex control (Fig. 4-3) uses a photocell with a hole in its center. Light from a lamp passes through a hole and a lens, and illuminates the target. Light reflected from the target passes back through the lens and falls upon the photocell. If the amount of light reflected to the photocell changes, the electrical characteristics of the

Fig. 4-3 Reflex photoelectric control: (a) light path to target; (b) light path from target to control.

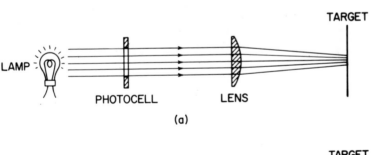

(a)

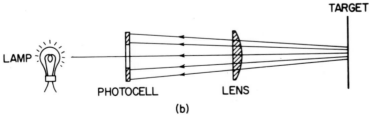

(b)

cell change, operating the output circuitry. Many materials may serve as the target as long as sufficient light is reflected to operate the photocell. Even smoke, or other particles in the air, may be used as a target.

The principal advantage of this type of control is its simplicity. The disadvantages of this type relate to the photocell with a hole in the center. Only bulk-effect type photosensors, such as selenium and silicon photovoltaic cells and photosensitive resistances, can be used. Further, these cells, which must be specially made, present manufacturing problems. A simple photocell could be used in place of the donut shape, but it would not interrupt the maximum amount of light.

A more efficient construction for the reflex photocontrol is shown in Fig. 4-4. A piece of "one-way," or half-silvered, glass is used to split the light beam. This glass passes light more easily in one direction than in the other. The light

Fig. 4-4 One-way mirror reflex photoelectric control: (a) path of light transmission; (b) path of light reflection (and reception).

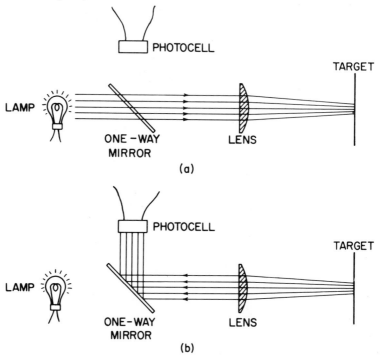

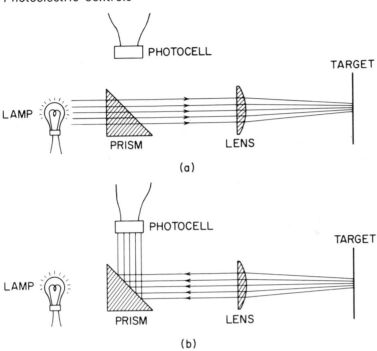

Fig. 4-5 Prism type reflex photoelectric control: (a) path of light transmission; (b) path of light reflection (and reception).

from the lamp passes through the glass and through the lens, striking the target. Light reflected from the target returns through the lens and strikes the glass. The glass reflects most of the light upwards toward the photocell. A substantial amount of light is lost when the light passes through the mirror and when it is reflected. However, a standard photocell may now be used.

Another efficient construction (Fig. 4-5) uses a triangular prism to separate the transmitted and received light beams. The operation is similar to the previous control, except that the prism is a more efficient beam splitter than the mirror and wastes less light.

PHOTOELECTRIC-CONTROL CIRCUITRY

The photocell is useless unless it is coupled with effective circuitry. What form the circuitry takes depends on the photocell used and the end result that is desired. The majority of photoelectric controls produced today use either a photosensitive resistor, photovoltaic cells, or photodiodes and phototransistors. Although a few applications may call for light-activated SCR's or photofets, these are rare. Each sensor has a number of commonly used, straightforward circuit configurations.

For example, the photosensitive resistor is most often used in a voltage divider (Fig. 4-6). A fixed voltage is applied across the photocell and a variable resistor. The voltage at the midpoint will depend on the ratio of the two resistances. Since one resistance decreases with increasing light, the output voltage will increase as light increases. The variable resistance may be used to normalize the output voltage for

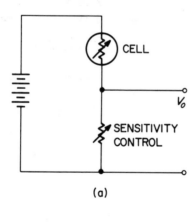

Fig. 4-6 (a) Photosensitive conductor in voltage divider circuit; (b) graph of output voltage versus incident light with sensitivity control resistance as a parameter.

(a)

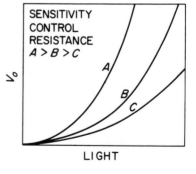

(b)

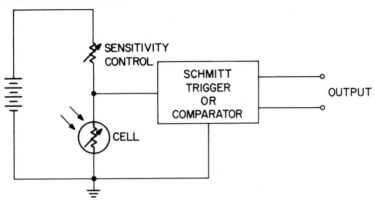

Fig. 4-7 Voltage divider circuit driving Schmitt trigger or comparator.

a fixed light intensity. It may also be used as a "sensitivity" control, as it will regulate the amount of light necessary for a given output voltage. The position of the photocell and the variable resistor may be interchanged to invert the operation. With the voltage divider, the photosensitive resistor's output effectively becomes a variable voltage. Therefore, the best circuit to sense the voltage output would probably be either a Schmitt trigger or a comparator (Fig. 4-7). The Schmitt trigger provides a rapid and positive action, while the comparator circuit allows a more precise setting of the trigger point with no hysteresis. However, if the circuitry

Fig. 4-8 Schmitt trigger photorelay (courtesy of Clairex Corporation).

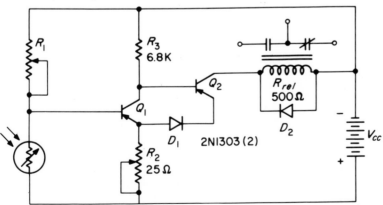

must drive a relay, both circuits will exhibit hysteresis because of the intrinsic hysteresis of the relay. Combining a relay with a comparator may result in a small operating region in which the relay pulls in or drops out slowly. This may be objectionable. However, the comparator will be much more insensitive to changes in supply voltage and ambient temperature than the Schmitt trigger. The comparison voltage is generally developed from the same voltage that is impressed across the photocell–resistor combination. This means that an increase in photocell output voltage due to a rise in supply voltage will be compared to a voltage which has risen the same percentage. Since the comparator is usually a differential device, its temperature dependence will be much smaller than that of the Schmitt trigger, which is usually single-ended.

A simple representative Schmitt-trigger circuit (Fig. 4-8) uses two transistors. If the first stage, Q_1 is saturated, then Q_2 will be off because its base–emitter junction is shorted. No collector or emitter current, except for leakage currents, flows in Q_2. The relay is thus de-energized. Also, the voltage drop across R_2 is due only to the emitter flow of Q_1. Since Q_1 is saturated, the collector–emitter voltage is about 0.1 volt. Assuming a high β, the collector current is equal to the emitter current. This current is $(V_{cc} - 0.1)/(R_2 + R_3)$. The voltage developed across R_2 is then

$$\frac{R_2}{R_2 + R_3}(V_{cc} - 0.1)$$

To maintain Q_1 in the saturated state, its base–emitter drop must be 0.3 volt, or the base must be 0.3 volt more negative than the emitter, or

$$\frac{R_2}{R_2 + R_3}(V_{cc} - 0.1) + 0.3$$

If the base voltage drops below this amount, Q_1 will start to come out of saturation, turning on Q_2 when the collector–emitter voltage is about 0.6 volt. The current through R_2

increases as Q_2 begins to conduct. The increase raises the emitter voltage of Q_1, turning it off, and also turning on Q_2 harder. The regenerative transition is inherent in the Schmitt trigger. After switching, Q_1 is off and Q_2 is saturated. The voltage across R_3 is now

$$\frac{R_2}{R_2 + R_{rel}} \, (V_{cc} - 0.1)$$

The input voltage must exceed this by 0.3 volt in order to turn on Q_1 again. The difference in transition voltages is the hysteresis voltage. The two diodes in the circuit serve different purposes. D_1 is used to increase the turn-on voltage of Q_2 by 0.6 volt. D_2 is normally back biased. When the relay coil is de-energized, the inductance of the relay attempts to maintain a constant current through the coil. Without D_2 a large reverse transient would be developed. D_2 serves to damp the reverse transient and to protect the transistors.

The Schmitt-trigger circuit has several shortcomings. The hysteresis voltage depends on the resistance of the relay. Since the coil resistance is generally temperature sensitive, so is the hysteresis voltage. The triggering voltage may be only a small fraction of the supply voltage, which could require a very high illumination level to achieve the necessarily low resistance. For applications where the light changes abruptly, fast action may be unnecessary, and a comparator circuit may be used.

The comparator compares V_1 with V_2. If V_1 is greater than V_2, Q_1 is on and Q_2 is off (see Fig. 4-9). Q_4 is also on, allowing current to flow through the relay coil. The emitters of Q_1 and Q_2 are supplied by Q_3, a field effect transistor (F.E.T.) constant-current source. This insures a good common mode range. V_1 is the voltage at the midpoint of R_1 and the photocell; it increases with decreasing light. V_2 is a variable reference voltage which can vary from zero to V_{cc}. Resistor R_5 can be set to operate the relay at a selected illumination level.

A photovoltaic cell may also be used as a light-sensitive resistor when it is reverse-biased. It may be used with the

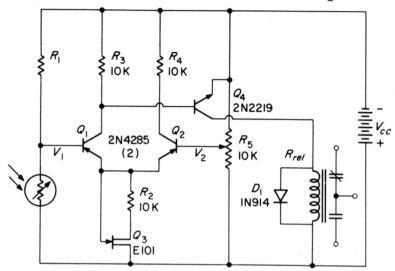

Fig. 4-9   Comparator photorelay. Control R_5 sets the firing point.

same type of circuitry as the photosensitive conductors. The advantage of the photovoltaic cell over the photosensitive conductor is the high linearity which makes the operation predictable and easily calculable. The temperature dependence may also be reduced. A photodiode can also be used in place of a photovoltaic cell to provide faster response.

The photovoltaic cell and photodiode may also be used as voltage generators. Their voltage output is logarithmically proportional to light intensity, and at maximum is only about 0.5 volt. A sensitive amplifier can be used to bring the output voltage up to about five volts, at which point a Schmitt trigger can be used.

Both photosensitive conductors and photovoltaic cells are highly temperature dependent. Although some photoelectric-control applications require operation only at room temperature, many controls must perform reliably even though the ambient temperature is very hot or very cold. A means of compensating for the changes in photocell performance must be used. Unfortunately the temperature coefficients of photocell parameters are rarely available or, when they are, are complicated in nature. This makes simple methods of temperature compensation, such as correction with thermistors, very difficult to apply. The solution most commonly applied is to use two photocells. One photocell is used as the light sensor. The other is not exposed to light, but is kept at the same ambient temperature as the other cell. The cells are used in such a way that the output of the circuitry is a function of the ratio of cell parameters. If the cell parameters change in absolute value because of a temperature change it will not affect the output. The drawbacks to this compensation method include the fact that the temperature coefficients may be a function of light levels. This is generally true of cadmium-sulfide and cadmium-selenide sensors. However, in a reflex type control the light source is close to the primary sensor. There is no reason why the compensating sensor cannot be illuminated by the light source also. Photosensitive conductors are hard to match as far as temperature coefficients go. Some manufacturers have placed two photocells in the same package so that compensation may be more easily attained. The best circuit for temperature compensation is a differential scheme, and a comparator (Fig. 4-9) may be used.

Broad-area silicon and selenium photovoltaic cells offer better temperature compensation possibilities. The reverse-bias output current is a function of light, temperature, and no-light leakage current. Since dual chips are readily available, the leakage currents can be well matched. Also, because of the cell's linearity, the temperature-dependent dark current can be subtracted from the current due to light, leaving a current due principally to illumination. Again, a good circuit configuration to use is the differential comparator (Fig. 4-9).

Thus, the outputs of the photocell are sometimes amplified, sometimes not; then they may be compensated for temperature, and then they are usually fed to a Schmitt trigger or comparator. Both the Schmitt trigger and the comparator have two main output states, which means that the photoelectric control mainly senses either the absence or presence of light. The Schmitt trigger or the comparator decides whether the signal from the sensor shows the presence or absence of light, and deals with the uncertain band, if any. The output of the Schmitt trigger or comparator is essentially useless because it is at a low power level. In order to control a sizable amount of power to actuate a valve, a solenoid, or perhaps a conveyor belt, an output stage must be used. The output stage, which provides the necessary power amplification, may be a relay, an SCR, a power transistor switch, or a fluid device. Further, the output stage may require a latching action or some form of time delay.

The relay is the simplest way to achieve high-power amplification. With a few milliamperes at a few volts, one may control many amperes and many volts. An open relay contact has practically infinite resistance, while closed contact resistances in the milliohm range are not uncommon. Because of its nature the relay suffers from slow response time, and it has only two states. Also, the contacts may "bounce" while switching from one state to the other, leading to possible transients and erratic operation. However, these disadvantages are not often important because a bistable operation is most commonly used, and the speed of the control is usually limited by the photocell. Common types of relays may be used at repetitive rates of sixty switches per second, while reed relays can be operated almost ten times faster. To operate the relay, a transistor switch is commonly used. Since the relay coil has considerable inductance, considerable transients may be generated when the current supplied to it is interrupted. These transients are given by $e = L\ (di/dt)$, where L is the relay coil inductance and di/dt is the time rate of current change. To reduce the effect of transients two methods may be used. A reverse-biased diode may be shunted across the coil. The diode does not conduct normally, but damps any reverse transient voltage which exceeds its forward-bias voltage. The second method is to reduce di/dt by shunting the transistor switch by a capacitor. When the transistor turns off, current may still flow through the relay and the capacitor. An alternative is to shunt the relay with a capacitor to absorb the transient. One can rarely get something for nothing. Any component which is added to reduce the relay's turn-off transient will also slow down its response so that it takes longer to drop out.

The SCR (silicon-controlled rectifier) is a very attractive component for industrial control. The power required to trigger it may be minute, but it may be able to outdo the relay in switching high power. Further, it has no moving parts, so its speed of response can be several orders of magnitude higher than that of a relay. The SCR can be connected back to back so that it can control ac circuitry. It is basically a latching device, very similar to the thyratron tube. When operated from a dc supply, it will remain on until the current passing through it drops below a certain holding level. When operated from an ac supply it does not latch, because it turns off at each cycle when the applied voltage goes through zero. It can also be used as a proportional device by controlling the phase angle of and thus triggering the ac wave. The SCR may be used to drive motors or solenoids as well as to drive a relay coil instead of a transistor.

A latch action is often needed in a photoelectric control. For example, once the light beam in a photoelectric burglar alarm is broken, the alarm should latch into the on state, even if the light path is later unblocked. The latch action can be obtained in the circuitry, in the output relay, or in combination. An inherently latching circuit, such as an SCR or a flip-flop can be used. A special latching relay, which can remain in the energized state after power is removed, can also be used. Or, a set of contacts on a nonlatching relay can be made to keep the relay energized after an initial actuation.

Time delays are also important in many applications. There are many different time-delay requirements. For example, a light beam may be broken for too short an interval to operate a relay. What is needed is a circuit to stretch the short pulse; for this purpose a pulse stretcher or monostable multivibrator is used. Similarly, the relay cannot drop out unless it has sufficient time. A monostable multivibrator can be used here too. Several more involved applications call for two or more time delays. These applications include the monitoring of automated production lines, the velocity of moving objects, and other sequential operations which are initiated by a photoelectric control.

If the time delay is electrically controlled, it will be generated by charging a capacitor to a certain voltage which then activates or triggers an active device or a relay. The most commonly used active devices include transistors, SCR's, and unijunction transistors. When stability of the time delay is desired, transistors and unijunctions are preferred because their firing voltages can be made high enough to make junction drops secondary. The forward-biased junction drops decrease by 2.0 mv/°C. The voltage across a capacitor which is charging toward a fixed voltage V is $V = Ve^{-t/RC}$. The time required to reach a certain voltage is proportional to the RC product and not the value of R or C alone. For a stable delay both R and C as well as V must be stable. The most potentially unstable component is the capacitor. For this reason electrolytic capacitors are avoided in favor of paper or plastic capacitors. Since these types are not readily available in high capacitance values, a large resistor must be used. This necessitates a high input impedance voltage sensor, because the impedance of the sensor is in parallel with the resistor.

Time-delay stages are generally included in the controller box. The most commonly provided time delay is used to prevent too short a pulse from actuating the output relay. The necessary pulse width is usually 25 milliseconds.

PHOTOELECTRIC-CONTROL
APPLICATIONS

The simplest and most common photoelectric-control systems use one or more pairs of light sources and sensors. Over the many years during which photoelectric controls have been used, a large number of standard applications and frequently used solutions have evolved. The majority of applications free human beings from trivial tasks or perform jobs that humans cannot. An example is a burglar or intruder alarm which operates when a person breaks the light beam. The resulting action may be the ringing of an alarm or siren. Or the control may be used as a door opener in stores, elevators, or factories. A hand breaking a light beam can cause a hazardous machine to shut down when the hand is too close for safety, or it can activate an electrical hand drier.

The path of the light beam does not have to go from the light source directly to the sensor. A mirror or prism may be used to bend the path around corners or to increase the path length. This has advantages when an irregular path must be monitored, or when the interruption may occur in a large area.

Photoelectric controls are often found on the factory production line. One of the prime uses is in high speed counting of objects moving past the light source and sensor. The output of the control is fed to a mechanical or electrical counter where the total count of objects is held. The rate at which the objects move will determine what types of counters and light sensors can be used. In general, mechanical counters can count at rates exceeding 1000 counts per minute. Although they are the simplest and least expensive units, they have a limited life and may make considerable noise when counting. When higher counting rates are needed, an electronic counter must be used. The counting rate can easily exceed millions per second. However, these counters are considerably more expensive than the mechanical ones. The control can supply a relay closure for operating a mechanical counter, but it is preferable to actuate the counter with a nonmechanical device such as a transistor or SCR. If a relay were used, the counting rate (maximum) would decrease, since roughly double the time would then be required for each count. When electronic counters are actuated at moderate or high rates, a nonmechanical switch is mandatory.

For counting rates under several thousand operations per minute, cadmium-sulfide or cadmium-selenide cells are quite adequate. For higher rates a broad-area silicon or selenium photovoltaic cell is suitable. Still higher rates demand a photodiode or phototransistor.

In order to register a count the light beam must be broken or sufficiently modified to work the control. Where the objects moving past the sensor have reasonably large gaps between them there is little problem. However, there are many instances where the objects are closely spaced. There may be no light path through the interobject spaces. The solution then is to sense the presence of the object not by shining light through the interstices, but by detecting one point on each object. When the object is rounded, as a bottle or a cylinder, the sensed point may be the high point on the circumference. If flat objects, such as cartons or boxes, are to be counted they can be marked with a light spot or dark spot to aid detection.

In many counting applications a certain total is desired. The simplest way to achieve an indication of the proper count is to use a preset or predetermining-type counter. This counter is set to count a certain number. When this number is counted, the counter supplies an output signal which may be used to shut down the conveyor, to apply a marking, to load the total count into a box or bottle, or some similar operation. The preset counter is often set to the complement of the desired number. Since the sum of a number and its complement is zero in a cyclic counter, the counter circuitry only has to sense, or decode, zero. To sense all the possible numbers would be inefficient. For example, suppose a counter with a maximum count of 10,000 before recycling was set to count to 375. The actual count that would be entered in the counter would be 10,000 — 375 or 9,625. When 375 additional counts accumulate, the count reaches 10,000, which is the same as zero.

Another production-line task for photoelectric controls is sorting and inspecting. When several different items are processed by one conveyor belt system, the photoelectric control can perform a sorting operation if it can discriminate between the objects. The easiest attribute the control can sense is the height, width or size. For example, the height can be monitored with a vertically arranged bank of light sources and sensors. With proper decoding, the height is determined by the lowest photocell which is illuminated. This scheme can only be used when the heights of the objects are widely different from each other. The number of photocells used determines the resolution, or how many different heights can be distinguished. The length of an object can be determined with a single photocell and a number of time-delay relays if the object moves past the photocell at a constant rate. At the instant the light from the source is blocked from the photocell, the relays are triggered. Each relay takes a certain time to energize. When the object passes the photocell and the light beam is then continuous a voltage is applied to the normally closed contacts of the relays, which are tied in series. The voltage appears across the contacts of the first relay which has not been energized, and gives an indication of the time that the object required to pass by the photocell. The product of the velocity and the time is the length of the object. If the velocity of the conveyor is not constant, then its speed may be sensed with a tachometer and used to feed all the time-delay relays, thus compensating for speed.

The output of the photoelectric control can be used to control routing of sorted items by operating gates or chutes on the conveyor. It can also be used to discard rejected items from the conveyor. Controls which detect items to be rejected or diverted are sometimes called inspection controls. Inspection controls are usually used to detect uncapped or unfilled bottles, or open cartons, or underfilled containers. Two sets of light sources and sensors are normally used for this application. The first set is used to detect the presence of the object. This set then energizes the second photocell, which looks for the necessary condition. The operation of the first photocell is the necessary condition for the operation of the second. Without the first photocell, a fault would be indicated every time an object passed from the light beam.

Another use of the photoelectric control on a conveyor line is to monitor when a tie-up, or "jamming," occurs. This may be caused by an obstruction in the flow or by the stoppage of a downstream conveyor belt. When jamming occurs, the objects on the belt do not move at their normal speed, if they move at all. The jamming monitor senses the velocity of an object moving past it, and is triggered when the velocity is too low. The control consists of a conventional photoelectric control with a time-delay relay. When the object breaks the light beam, the time-delay relay is actuated. If the beam is still broken when the timing cycle is completed, a tie-up is assumed. Another relay, triggered simultaneously by the broken light beam and the expired time delay, will now indicate a jamming condition. The operation of this relay depends upon the spacing of the objects so that the light beam is interrupted when the objects pass. If the time-delay relay is reset when the light beam is restored, there will be no effect or false indication if the conveyor belt speeds up.

Closely related to the jamming control is the control which senses an absence of objects on a conveyor line. Again, the control uses a photocell–source pair and a time-delay relay. The time-delay relay is actuated when no object is present. If an object fails to break the beam before the time delay expires, the control relay is energized. The conditions necessary to energize the control relay are an unbroken light beam and an expired time delay. If objects are moving down the conveyor belt at a certain rate, the light beam will always be broken before the time delay expires. When the beam is broken, the time delay is reset; timing does not resume until the light beam is unbroken. The components required for this control are identical to those in the jamming control, except that the action of the photocell and light source is inverted.

Besides counting, the photoelectric control can be used for measuring. The object to be measured is fitted with a device which breaks a light beam according to linear measure. Two such devices (Fig. 4-10) are a wheel with holes in it, and a tape with alternating areas of light and dark. The wheel, in conjunction with a photoelectric control, makes an excellent sensor of roll lengths for yard goods or paper. The wheel has an accurate circumference and a number of equally spaced holes. If the wheel is placed in contact with a

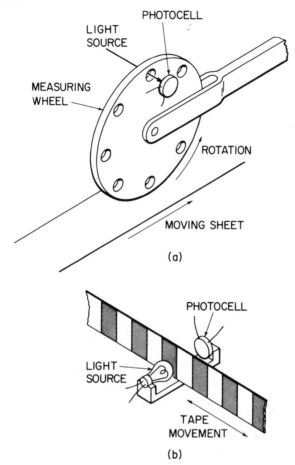

PHOTOCELL

LIGHT
SOURCE

MEASURING
WHEEL

ROTATION

MOVING SHEET

(a)

PHOTOCELL

LIGHT
SOURCE

TAPE
MOVEMENT

(b)

Fig. 4-10 (a) Wheel with holes regularly spaced in rim accurately measures linear data when used with photoelectric control and pulse counter. (b) Tape with opaque and transparent areas serves as incremental position sensor with photoelectric control.

moving sheet of paper, cloth, or other material, it will rotate at a speed proportional to the speed of the sheet. As the wheel rotates, the position of the holes changes, and the light beam is allowed to pass from the light source to the light sensor when the hole passes. During one rotation of the wheel the beam is broken as many times as there are holes in the wheel. The output of the photocell is fed to a counter. The counter accumulates the number of times the light beam is broken. Since this number is proportional to the number of rotations, and since the outer rim of the wheel travels a certain distance for each rotation, the total length of the sheet that has passed the wheel is known. For example, assume a wheel whose circumference is 12 inches, and which has twelve equally spaced holes. If three feet of material pass beneath the wheel, the light beam will be broken 36 times. When used in conjunction with a counter, an accurate measure of the length that has passed beneath the wheel will be known. If the counter can be preset, then it may be used to actuate a shear or paper cutter when the proper length has been reached. This type of length measurement is incremental, because the control can only respond in steps whose size is determined by the circumference and number of holes in the wheel.

The tape device is principally used as a position sensor or control. Each time the tape moves a certain distance, the light beam is broken. By counting the number of pulses produced, the total amount of movement is known. Since a large number of light and dark bands can be produced easily on the tape or film, the resolution can be high. The tape cannot be used to measure the length of a continuous piece of material, as the wheel can. Also, in this simple form the tape (and the wheel) cannot discriminate the direction of the motion. To do this an arrangement using two photo-cells is necessary.

A photoelectric control can be used to maintain loops in material produced in rolls. Loops are often needed to prevent too much tension from stretching or tearing the roll. Two photocell and light source pairs are used (Fig. 4-11a). The loop is arranged so that, when it is the proper length, the light beam to the top photocell will be blocked but the light beam to the second will be clear. If the loop gets larger, the light beam to the bottom photocell will be interrupted. The power to the feed roller will be cut, which will reduce the loop size. If the loop gets small enough to allow light to pass to the top photocell, the power to the take-up roller will be cut, allowing the loop to get longer.

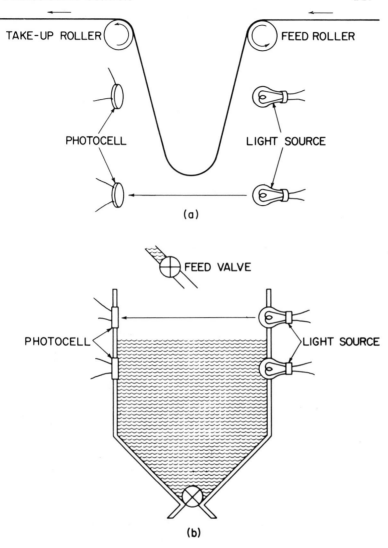

Fig. 4-11 (a) Photoelectric loop control keeps the loop between two photocells and two light sources. If both light beams are broken, loop is too long and feed roller slows down. If no light beams are broken, loop is too short and feed roller speeds up. (b) Two photoelectric controls maintain tank level between limits. If both light beams are broken, overflow valve opens. If both beams are unbroken, feed valve opens.

For successful operation, the speed of the take-up roller should be nearly the same as the speed of the feed roller.

Of course, if the two speeds were always equal, the size of the loop would remain constant. If the speeds are widely different, the control must start and stop both rollers with great frequency, which may place a strain on the machinery. The purpose of a constant-length loop might also be defeated since a strain might be placed on the material in the loop.

When a constant level in a tank or bin is desired, a photoelectric control is often used. It is often preferred over a simpler type of float valve when liquids are to be kept at a constant level. The liquid may be corrosive, or a control with no moving parts may be desired. Two photocells and light sources may be used to keep the liquid (or solid) level between set limits (Fig. 4-11b). If the light beam of the lower photocell is passed, then the feed valve is opened, allowing more material to flow into the container. If the light beam to the top photocell is obstructed, the feed valve is closed, allowing the level to subside. This type of control is especially useful in controlling the level in bins containing dry material, because the dry material usually jams or clogs a mechanical level sensor such as a ball float.

A photoelectric control can make an excellent smoke or haze detector. If the air between a light source and sensor has smoke particles or haze in it, the light beam will be attenuated. If the control has sufficient sensitivity, it can respond to the drop in light intensity which corresponds to the amount of smoke in the air. A reflex type of control is suited for this use, as smoke or haze is a fairly good reflector. In fact, the light reflection of smoky air is easier to monitor than the decrease in light conductivity, because the percentage of light change is greater for the former case.

LIGHT MEASUREMENTS

Discussing light-sensitive devices and beams of light in general terms cannot convey a great deal of information to us. To more precisely measure the properties of devices involving light, we must use the precise terms, namely the candlepower, the foot-candle, and the lumen.

The candlepower is a measure of light intensity. In the past it was equal to the intensity produced by the burning of a standard candle. The candlepower is now defined with a special bulb. The candlepower of these bulbs is usually measured from a certain direction in the horizontal plane of the lamp's filament.

The foot-candle is a measure of the brightness of light at a given point. This light is assumed to come from a point source. Since the brightness will be directly proportional to the intensity of the source (in candlepower) and inversely proportional to the square of the distance between the source and the receptor, we can write " (Foot-candles) = (Candlepower)/(Distance)^2." Another measure of brightness is the watt per square meter, which has the same dimensions as the foot-candle.

The lumen is a measure of the light flux passing through a given area. If a sphere enclosed a light source with a brightness of one candlepower, then 4π lumens would flow through the spherical surface. Thus, the lumens are directly proportional to the intensity of the enclosed light source and also directly proportional to the surface area.

5

Temperature Controls

The ability to control the temperature of an object or an area is extremely important in countless applications. The end result of the temperature control may be increased comfort, the proper functioning of an industrial process, or longer component life. We say that the function of temperature controls is to maintain a *constant* temperature, but by "*constant* temperature" we mean a *band* of temperatures about a nominal value. Depending on how narrow this temperature band must be, a simple or complicated scheme may be required.

The simplest temperature control is a thermostat. The thermostat is usually a bimetallic strip or disc which opens or closes an electrical contact, depending on its temperature. The bimetallic strip is composed of strips of two dissimilar metals which have different temperature coefficients of expansion. Since the strips are bound together, usually by a spot weld, they can only be straight when they have the same length. Because they have different coefficients of expansion, this happens at one temperature only. At all other temperatures the strips will have a bend. A contact is often placed on the end of a bimetallic strip so that it can touch another contact if the bend is sufficient. The strip can be moved further away from or closer to the other contact so that contact will be made at differing temperatures. This simple sensing control combines a sensor and an output device. The bimetallic disc is a significant improvement over the bimetallic strip. The strip bends very slowly as the temperature changes and may tend to "creep" into or out of the closed position. One disadvantage of creeping is imprecision. There is a gray area where the contact is not fully closed or open. Another disadvantage is seen when the contacts are carrying appreciable power or switching a moderate voltage. If the contacts are half open there will be an arc across them which may ruin the contacts, cause undesired transients, and generate radio-frequency interference for as long as the arc exists. On the other hand, the switching of the bimetallic disc is rapid because there is no ambiguous point. One of the disc's disadvantages is the fact that it is difficult to modify the operating temperature over as wide a range as for the bimetallic strip.

In constant-temperature controls, the electrical contacts of the thermostat are used to activate a heater system or a cooling system. There is only one mode of operation—either on or off. No intermediate quantity of heat may be added to or removed from the controlled volume. Further, thermostats exhibit two undesirable properties: slow time response, and considerable hysteresis. This is mainly due to the mechanical nature of the thermostat.

An electronic analog of the thermostat may be easily constructed by coupling a temperature sensor to a decision-making circuit such as a Schmitt trigger or a comparator. A typical circuit, which employs a thermistor in a Wheatstone bridge as the sensor, and an integrated-circuit comparator, is shown in Fig. 5-1. This circuit will switch when $R_2 R_3 / R_1 = R_T$ where R_T is the resistance of the thermistor. The response time is mainly determined by the speed of the thermistor, which is a function of its thermal mass. A small-size thermistor has less thermal mass than a large one. Other sensors can be used in place of the thermistor.

A thermostatic control has only two states: fully off or

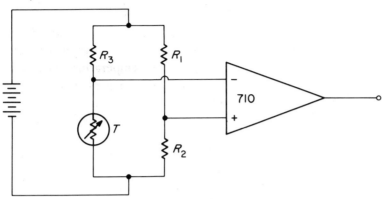

Fig. 5-1 Electronic thermostat analog using thermistor and integrated circuit comparator.

fully on. A typical temperature control system with this type of control may have four components. They are the sensor, the control circuits, the heater (or cooler), and the controlled volume. Heat may be added to or taken from the control volume at an unpredictable rate and time. The purpose of the control is to add (or take away) such heat as is necessary to maintain the desired temperature.

The sensor is located in one part of the controlled volume and the heater (or cooler) in another. If the heater is suddenly energized, the temperature of the volume will not also change instantaneously. Since temperature can only be measured at a point, the temperature of the volume is assumed to be the average temperature of all points or the temperature at the sensor. The temperature change due to the added heat will be most noticeable very close to the source of the heat. The points farthest away from the heat source will experience a temperature change only after a considerable time has passed. The length of the delay depends on the distance between the source and the distant point, and on many other parameters. The delay between the time that heat is supplied and the time it is noticed at a remote point is called thermal lag. It is possible to calculate thermal lag, but the calculations are not simple, and it is easier to estimate thermal lag experimentally.

The thermal lag has an important effect on the control

of temperature. For example, it will cause an oscillation in temperature when the temperature is controlled by an on–off or binary type control, such as a thermostat. A typical system has a thermostat with a negligible temperature hysteresis and a thermal lag τ. The thermostat triggers at T_1. If the control-volume average temperature is lower, the heater is energized. Heat is added to the control volume at a rate faster than it is being removed. After a time, the temperature of the thermostat is T_1. The heater is de-energized. Because the thermal lag prevents the added heat from spreading instantaneously throughout the volume, the temperatures within the volume may not have reached equilibrium when the thermostat temperature is T_1. It may continue to rise after the heater is de-energized. However, since no new heat is being added, and heat is being slowly removed, the temperature reaches a maximum point and then starts to decrease. The decrease continues until the temperature at the thermostat is T_1. The heater is again energized. The thermal lag again causes a time delay between the application of power and the temperature change. Therefore, the temperature may drop further before it starts to rise. This is shown graphically in Fig. 5-2. The on–off action is continuous and does not damp out in a few cycles. The ratio of on time to off time may change because it depends on the rate of heat loss as well as on the thermal lag of the added heat.

If thermal lag were not present in the system, the temperature would not oscillate, but the heater would be switched on and off to set the rate of heat added equal to the rate of heat lost. The temperature oscillations often add more temperature variations to the controlled volume than were there without the control.

Thermostatic controls may reduce temperature variations to amounts from one to several degrees. In many instances this is not sufficient. It may be required that the temperature stay constant within small fractions of a degree. To achieve this close regulation a *proportional* temperature control must be used. The binary or thermostatic control can only respond to temperature changes with either a full on or a full off

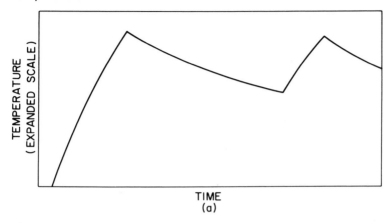

TIME
(a)

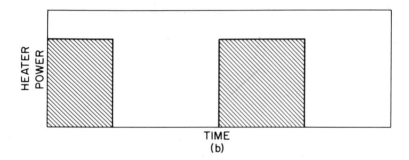

TIME
(b)

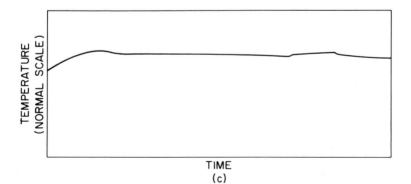

TIME
(c)

Fig. 5-2 Characteristics of binary temperature control system showing variation of temperature with time: (a) temperature
(expanded scale); (b) heater power; (c) temperature (normal
scale).

command. The proportional control has the ability to add or take away the required amount of heat (see Fig. 5-3). A large number of graduated steps between full off and full on may be applied. The advantage of the proportional control is that the action is smooth and without discontinuities, in contrast to the case of the binary control. The amount of heat which is added is proportional to the difference between the actual sensed temperature and the desired temperature. Mathematically, $Q = K_1(T_1 - T_2)$, where Q is the heat added, T_1 is the desired temperature, T_2 is the measured temperature, and K_1 is the constant with the dimensions BTU/°F. The effects of both thermal lag and thermal inertia have been neglected.

Fig. 5-3 Proportional temperature control system block diagram.

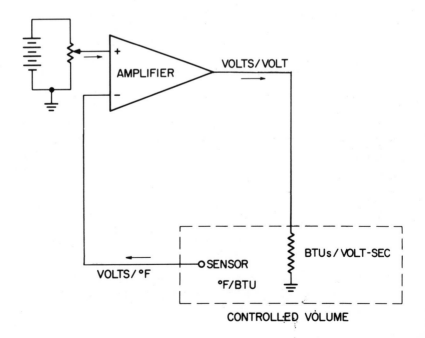

The gain of the system is the product of many gains. For example, the temperature transducer may have a transfer function of so many volts per degree Fahrenheit. The electronic amplifier which measures the difference between the actual temperature-produced voltage and a reference voltage has a gain expressed in volts per volt. The heater which is controlled by the amplifier output has a transfer function in watts per volt. There is a relationship between watts and BTU's. The controlled volume has a transfer function in BTU's per degree Fahrenheit. All the elements may be represented as a loop. If the loop is broken at any point, the gain of the system may be measured, or it may be numerically calculated if the transfer functions are known. If it is large, the desired temperature will be maintained. For one percent accuracy, the gain must be greater than 100.

PROPORTIONAL-CONTROL SYSTEM

A representative proportional-control system might use a junction diode as the temperature transducer, and an integrated-circuit differential amplifier to subtract the sensor output voltage from the set voltage (see Fig. 5-4). The output of the amplifier is fed to a power transistor which controls a resistance heater in the controlled volume. The diode has a sensitivity of 2 millivolts per degree centigrade, and the amplifier has a gain of 1000. Therefore, if there is a difference of one degree centigrade between the desired temperature and the actual temperature, a two-volt signal will be developed at the amplifier output. The amplifier's maximum temperature sensitivity is 10 millivolts per degree centigrade, so ambient-temperature changes will have less than a one-half per cent effect on the operation, even if the amplifier is mounted in the controlled environment. A potentiometer is used to set the desired temperature. The power transistor which controls the heater is also mounted in the controlled volume. The reason for this is that the transistor's power dissipation is comparable to the heater dissipation. The

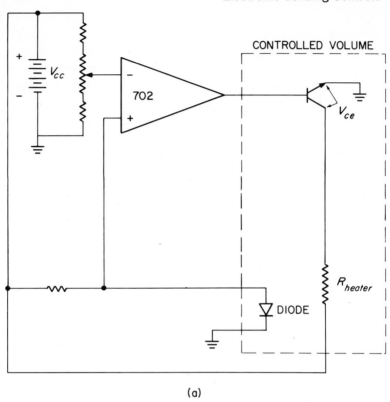

(a)

Fig. 5-4 (a) Proportional temperature control schematic diagram; (b—opposite) graph of power dissipation versus V_{ce} for 1 ohm heater resistance.

transistor dissipation is $(V_{ce})(i_c)$, where i_c is equal to

$$\frac{V_{cc} - V_{ce}}{R_{heater}}$$

Thus the transistor power dissipation is equal to

$$\frac{V_{ce}(V_{cc} - V_{ce})}{R_{heater}}$$

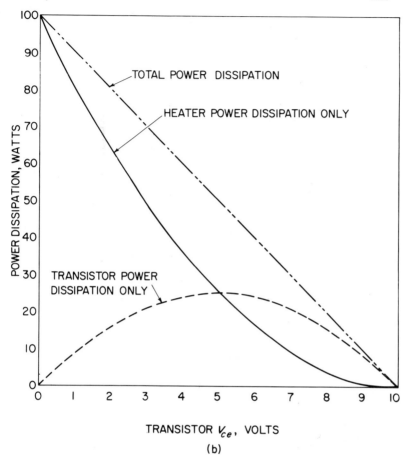

TRANSISTOR V_{ce}, VOLTS

(b)

The power dissipated in the resistance heater is equal to

$$\frac{(V_{cc} - V_{ce})^2}{R_{heater}}$$

When V_{ce} is half of V_{cc}, then the transistor dissipation is equal to the heater dissipation. Therefore, the transistor is used as a heating element as well as a power-control element. The total power dissipation added to the volume is

$$P_{diss} = \frac{(V_{cc} - V_{ce})^2 + V_{ce}(V_{cc} - V_{ce})}{R_{heater}}$$

This method of controlling the heater requires a high power dissipation in the transistor. When high powers are required from the heater, the necessary transistors are expensive. Fortunately, there are more efficient ways to control power. One way is to use a transistor as a switching element only. When the transistor is saturated, it carries full load current, but its voltage drop is small. When it is off, full supply voltage passes across it, but its current is negligible. Since the power dissipation is the product of voltage and current, the dissipation for both cases is small. The instantaneous power dissipated by the heating element is either zero or a maximum when it is operated by the switching transistor. If the heater were energized by a string of pulses, the instantaneous power would also be a string of pulses. However, the heater temperature and the temperature of the controlled volume cannot change as rapidly as the instantaneous power. Instead, they change with the average power that is applied. The average power is· the average overtime of the instantaneous power that is applied. If the heater has a long enough response time, the average power is the ratio of the off time to the on time. The sum of the off time and the on time is the period of the control. If the period is short with respect to the thermal time constant of the heater, then the on–off switching will be averaged out. For reasonable averaging, the period should be less than one-tenth the thermal time constant. For many applications, the period of a 60-cycle power line is high enough for satisfactory operation.

A control which switches the heater but which is also proportional is called a proportional switching control. The difference between the actual temperature and the desired temperature is used to control the on-to-off time of a switched heater. If the difference is great, the ratio of on time to off time is large. If the temperature difference is small, the off time is large and the on time is small. Although the period need not be constant, it is often more convenient to work with a constant period. The temperature difference between the desired and actual temperatures may be used to generate a voltage. This voltage is then fed to a *pulse-width modulator* in order to develop the variable pulse-width signal.

A typical proportional switching control (Fig. 5-5a) uses a differential amplifier to subtract a voltage corresponding to the actual temperature from a fixed voltage corresponding to the desired temperature. The output, which is the difference multiplied by one thousand, is used to control a variable constant-current source. The current source is used to charge a capacitor, producing a linear ramp voltage. The greater the output of the difference amplifier, the greater the current flowing in the capacitor will be. The slope of the voltage ramp is proportional to the charging current. The charging current is proportional to the difference between the desired temperature and the actual temperature. The capacitor is periodically discharged by a transistor switch which is controlled by a free-running oscillator. This turns the voltage ramp into a sawtooth whose slope depends on the temperature difference. The sawtooth voltage is fed to an emitter-follower with a Zener diode in the emitter lead. The diode shifts the sawtooth to negative by an amount equal to the sum of the Zener voltage and the base–emitter drop. This is then fed to the base of the switching transistor, which conducts when its base–emitter junction is forward-biased by more than 0.6 volt. When this transistor switches, power is applied to the heater. Power is turned off when the capacitor is discharged by the sawtooth. If the slope of the sawtooth is high, the switch will turn on early in the cycle. If the slope is moderate, the transistor will switch in the middle of the cycle. Finally, the slope can be so low that the transistor will not turn on at all.

Pulse-width modulation provides a means of attaining a highly variable, good-resolution control with high efficiency in the switching stage. In addition, the amount of power which is controlled can be much larger than is possible with an all-linear proportional control. For example, assume that the power transistor used can carry one ampere and sustain 100 volts from collector to emitter. The power dissipation of this transistor may be on the order of five watts. This

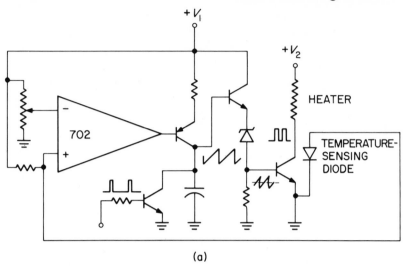

(a)

Fig. 5-5 Proportional switching control: (a) schematic diagram; (b, c, d—opposite) graph of power output versus pulse width modulator slope—(b) high, (c) medium, and (d) low slopes.

means that it can control a twenty-watt load when operated in a linear control. However, when operated in the switching mode it can control 100 watts, and the maximum dissipation will be lower than in the linear control.

The most commonly used sensors in temperature controls are thermocouples and resistance thermometers, or thermistors. The output of a thermocouple is on the order of 0.5 millivolt per degree centigrade. The total resistance change for a resistance thermometer may be a few per cent of its total resistance over its total temperature range. This means that simple solutions may not always apply themselves to resistance thermometer or thermocouple systems. Their low sensitivity places a burden on the circuitry which they operate. However, this is more than compensated for by the resultant high linearity.

With either of the two sensitive transducers, considerable amplification must be used in order to achieve a usable output level. Not only must the gain remain very constant, but the drift of the amplifier must be very small too. The maximum allowable drift for an amplifier to be used with a 0.5

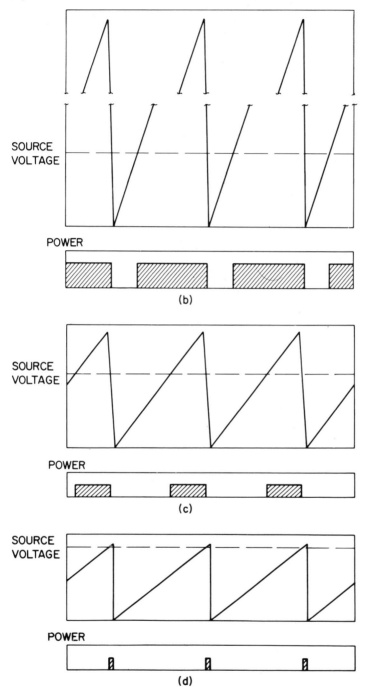

SOURCE
VOLTAGE

POWER

(b)

SOURCE
VOLTAGE

POWER

(c)

SOURCE
VOLTAGE

POWER

(d)

mv/°C thermocouple should be 50 microvolts or less for good precision.

One method of amplification uses a well matched and balanced differential amplifier. The voltage drift of these amplifiers may be as low as a few microvolts per degree centigrade. However, a voltage offset may exist across its terminals; this can be on the order of millivolts. The offset is multiplied by the gain of the amplifier in the same way as the input signal is. Fortunately this offset can be trimmed out with an adjusting potentiometer, but each amplifier must be trimmed individually, and the trimming must be repeated from time to time.

Offset voltages and offset drift are problems which occur only in directly coupled amplifiers. The design of low-drift, stable amplifiers is much simpler with alternating current. A thermocouple's output is direct current and cannot be amplified with an ac-coupled amplifier. However, if the direct-current output is modulated, the modulated signal can be ac-coupled for amplification (see Fig. 5-6). The modulator preserves the amplitude of the signal but switches it on and off. These modulators, which are generally called choppers, can be constructed in many ways. A very simple chopper can be made with a relay contact. The relay, usually a reed type, is switched off and on at a modulation frequency which is often 60 Hz. Another method of chopping the signal is to use a light to drive a photosensitive conductor. The resistance of the photocell goes from very high (no light) to low (light on), and modulates the signal. One disadvantage of these choppers is that their speed, or modulation frequency, is limited. When it is desired to chop the signal at rates greater than 100 Hz, an FET or bipolar transistor

Fig. 5-6 Thermocouple system with chopper to modulate dc thermocouple voltage.

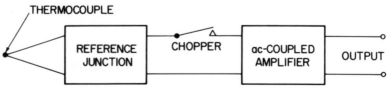

chopper is used. A bipolar transistor chopper has significant offset, which is the major disadvantage of its use.

It is not necessary to chop the output of a resistance thermometer. The resistance element is usually used in a bridge arrangement. To effect an ac output, all that is necessary is to drive the bridge from an ac source. The slight resistance change in the element will cause a proportional change in output voltage.

After the signal from the sensitive transducers has been converted to ac and amplified, it must often be converted back to dc. The component which converts the signal back to dc is often called a demodulator. It may consist of one or several diodes, another chopper, or a "perfect" diode simulated by an operational amplifier. After demodulation, it may be necessary to filter the signal to remove the modulation-frequency components.

One disadvantage of the chopper-stabilized amplifier is its slow response time. If the input signal changes when the signal is being chopped, the change may never appear in the output. In order to recover the signal with little distortion, the chopping rate should be much higher than the highest-frequency component of the input signal.

The resistance change in the thermistor is so great that it is rarely necessary to employ chopper-stabilization techniques. Often a simple directly coupled amplifier may be used with the thermistor in a bridge arrangement (see Fig. 5-7).

Fig. 5-7 Thermistor connected in Wheatstone bridge driven by ac source; as excitation allows use of low-drift ac coupled amplifiers.

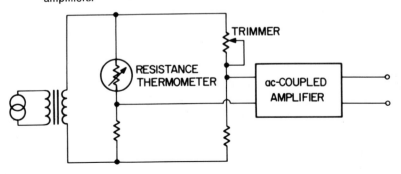

INDICATING CONTROLLERS

A thermostat may control the temperature of a volume, but it cannot indicate what temperature is actually sensed. A thermometer can indicate the temperature but cannot control it. There are many instances where the temperature must be both controlled and monitored. The device which does both is the indicating controller, or set-point temperature controller. These controllers may utilize either thermocouples or resistance thermometers. If thermocouples are used, automatic cold-junction reference is often provided in the unit. Following the transducer, a linear amplifier is used to boost the signal level. This amplifier may be chopper stabilized or otherwise drift compensated. The output of the amplifier is fed to a meter movement. Because of the excellent linearity of temperature transducers, the meter scale can usually be linear.

Temperature control is provided at one or more "set points." These set points may be moved over the meter face to correspond to a certain temperature. When the pointer which indicates temperature moves over the set-point pointer, the control is activated. Although the activation can be accomplished with a contact, the contact may affect the accuracy of the movement. Therefore, some form of contactless sensing of the indicator position is often used. A light source may be coupled to the pointer, and a photocell connected to the set point. When the pointer is at the set point, the light will illuminate the photocell, causing actuation of the control relay. The relay may be used to keep the set temperature constant, or it may be used to signal an operator or trigger an alarm. The position of the temperature pointer may also be sensed by inductive means. In this case a metallic flag is mounted on the pointer. The set points are movable transformer windings. When the temperature is at the set point, the flag separates the primary transformer winding from the secondary. The transformer is used in a critically coupled oscillator. When the flag separates the primary and secondary windings, the coupling is reduced and the oscillation ceases. This causes a relay to operate.

These approaches are mainly modifications of an electronic thermometer for use as a controller. A different and more direct approach would be to operate the temperature-indicating meter and the controller in parallel. A stage of amplification would be required to condition the output of the thermocouple or resistance thermometer. This would drive both the meter and a set-point comparator. The output of the comparator would drive the relay. This method depends on the linearity of the sensor. Also, another dial is required for the setting of the set point. The advantage of the indirect approach is that only one dial is required, which makes a small size feasible. In large indusrial systems there may be great numbers of temperature controllers, so the size of the controller and the ease of setting it are important.

Sensing controls which employ temperature-sensitive sensors are not only used to maintain constant temperatures. Many other areas of application are possible. For example, a temperature-sensitive device may be used as a level sensor. A thermistor is used in the probe (Fig. 5-8). The thermistor is operated in the self-heating condition. That is, it dissipates enough power so that its resistance is primarily determined by how fast heat can be removed from it. When the probe is surrounded by free air, its temperature is relatively high because very little heat is transferred to the air. Thus, its resistance is low. If the thermistor is placed into some other substance, the amount of heat that is transferred to the surroundings will increase or decrease. In most cases it will increase, causing the thermistor to cool. The cooling causes the thermistor's resistance to rise. The rise can be used to activate a relay or other output device.

To keep the level in a tank or bin between two limits, two of these controls may be used. The first control is longer than the second. When it is exposed to air, the level in the tank is too low, and the tank is filled. When the shorter probe is not exposed to air, the tank is too full, and the flow to the tank is stopped. This type of control is much more reliable than a conventional float control because there are no moving parts.

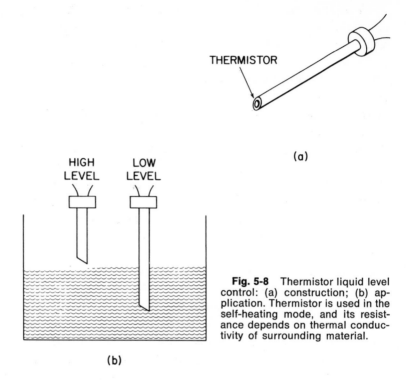

(a)

(b)

Fig. 5-8 Thermistor liquid level control: (a) construction; (b) application. Thermistor is used in the self-heating mode, and its resistance depends on thermal conductivity of surrounding material.

Another application of the temperature control is the measurement of liquid flow (see Fig. 5-9). Two temperature sensors are used in a length of pipe. The first sensor measures the temperature of the fluid. Further down the pipe, an electric heater adds heat to the liquid. The amount of heat energy added is proportional to the product of the power and the length of time over which it was added, in watt-seconds. The rate at which the heater adds heat to the liquid is constant. The temperature rise of the fluid is proportional to the product of the mass times the heat. Since the heat added is constant, the only thing which can change the temperature rise is a change in the mass of the fluid. This mass is actually the mass per unit time that flows past the heater. Assuming constant density, the mass per unit time

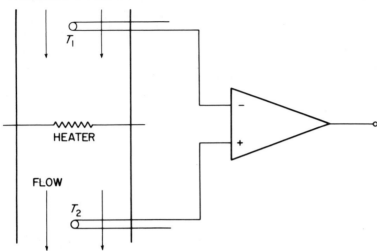

Fig. 5-9 Thermal flow meter measures temperature rise in fluid caused by adding known amount of heat to liquid with known specific heat but unknown flow rate. The greater the heat rise, the lower the flow.

is proportional to the rate of fluid flow. Thus the flow rate is measured by measuring the temperature difference between two points. If the output of the temperature sensor is a voltage, the two voltages can be subtracted, and the difference can operate a Schmitt trigger or comparator to drive a relay or silicon-controlled rectifier.

6

Electromechanical Controls

Electromechanical controls operate on such physical phenomena as position, speed, velocity, pressure, acceleration,
and vibration. They may be characterized by the input
transducers which are mechanically coupled to the sensed
phenomena. The electronic sensing controls may be intended to replace purely mechanical ones for greater sensitivity, repeatability, and longer life. Or they may find applications where no all-mechanical control could be used.

Position controls are widely used. Some common sensors
for linear-position determination are the linear variable
differential transformer, the linear potentiometer, and rotary
units with rack-and-pinion mechanisms. The output of these
sensors is, or can be converted to, a voltage which is proportional to position. The voltage may be ac or dc for the
potentiometer or ac for the linear variable differential transformer. If the output of the sensor is fed to a comparator
or Schmitt trigger, there will be an output when the desired
position is reached. A common application for this type of
control is to indicate a limit or a certain length. The point
which is sensed may be easily changed by changing the reference voltage.

Another area of application for position controls is in follower systems, where motion is sensed and transmitted electrically to a point where it is duplicated. Systems of this sort may be called servomechanisms. The basic follower system consists of an input sensor, an output sensor, a difference amplifier, and an actuator (see Fig. 6-1). For our discussion, we assume that both transducers are linear, and that the actuator position (or displacement) is required to follow the position of the input sensor within a certain allowed error.

The output of the input transducer, which may be either a potentiometer or linear variable differential transformer, is KVX_i, where K is a constant, V is the applied voltage, and X is the position of the input arm. Similarly, the output voltage of the output transducer is KVX_o, where K, V, and X are the same as before. Therefore, the voltage across the terminals of the difference amplifier is $KV(X_i - X_o)$. This

Fig. 6-1 Simple position following system with on-off actuation.

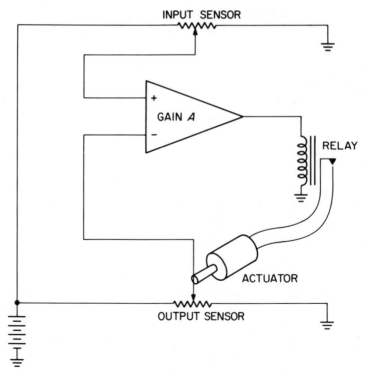

INPUT SENSOR

GAIN *A*

RELAY

ACTUATOR

OUTPUT SENSOR

difference voltage is multiplied by the gain A and used to drive the relay. The relay, in turn, controls the output actuator. This relay may require V_1 volts to energize and V_2 to de-energize. When the error voltage exceeds the former, the relay energizes the actuator to reduce the error. When the error voltage is below V_2 volts, the actuator is unpowered. These voltages can be translated to distance by dividing by the sensor constants. Thus, the actuator will be energized at M units and will be de-energized at N units:

$$M = \frac{V_1}{KVA} \quad N = \frac{V_2}{KVA}$$

The output arm will follow the position of the input arm, except that there will be an error and also a region where the input arm can be moved without causing any corresponding motion of the output arm. This area of no reaction is called a "dead band."

Most position controls use a rotary sensor such as a rotary potentiometer or a synchro. If a linear sensor is desired, some form of gearing can be used. The sensors may have either continuous rotation or a fixed number of turns, typically from one to ten. The linearity of these controls may be better than 0.1 per cent. This means that position may be fixed to within approximately one part in a thousand. For greater precision a digital encoder may be used. A digital encoder is a sensor whose output is in discrete, or digitized, form, as compared to a potentiometer or synchro, whose outputs are reasonably smooth and continuous. The output of most encoders is in binary form. A number of output lines correspond to binary digits. Each binary number corresponds to a certain position, or angle of shaft rotation. The encoder is basically a rotary switch. The switch may have many coaxial segments with a set of wipers for each segment, in a simple encoder. For example, a three-bit encoder might be one that has three concentric tracks. The tracks are segmented so that from zero to three wipers could be making contact, depending on the angle of rotation. There will be eight discrete positions, an amount equal to two raised to the number of bits $(2^3 = 8)$. Actual encoders, while functionally similar to the three-bit model, are much more complicated. The number of bits may be on the order of fifteen. With fifteen bits of position data, roughly one part in thirty-two thousand can be resolved. The construction of actual encoders may use mechanical wipers, or the encoder can be made with photoelectric-switch closures. The photoelectric encoder is attractive because there are no parts to wear, except bearings. This eliminates one problem of the switch-type encoder: poor contact resistance due to worn-down wiper brushes. Another refinement is to use a code in the encoder so that possible errors are minimized. For example, the encoder disc may be programmed so that only one bit changes at a time. This type of code may be called a Gray code.

The output of the encoder provides position data which may be far more accurate than continuous-position sensors can give. However, it is much harder to use the data. The output of the encoder is usually a logic output on a large number of lines. To use the output of the encoder, these logic outputs must first be assembled in the proper order. The output of the encoder is meaningless when the encoder is in transition from one state to the other. Therefore, the position data must be taken from the encoder only when it is not in a transitory position. To accomplish this, the encoder may furnish an interrogation signal, which indicates that position data may be taken. However, an output is usually required from the encoder at all times. This is why a memory is often used between the encoder and the output circuitry. The memory stores the position data while the encoder changes position, and updates the position data upon receiving an interrogation signal. This assures that there will always be an output.

The output of the encoder and buffer may be compared with other signals, added to other signals, or subtracted from other signals. This is conveniently done digitally, if the other signal is in digital form. Alternatively, a digital-to-analog converter may convert the shaft-encoder output back to analog form.

So far we have discussed position controls which operate only in discrete jumps or steps. These controls produce an error from output to input of the system because the system's position input can change continuously. In order to reduce the input to output error, an output actuator which can change position continuously must be used. Such a continuous position-following system (Fig. 6-2) has two position to voltage transducers to convert both the input position and the output position to voltage. The voltage difference between the sensor outputs corresponds to the position error. The difference voltage is established and amplified by a differential amplifier. This amplified difference is used to drive an actuator, usually a servomotor. A stage of power amplification may be required between the motor and the differential amplifier. A simple analysis will show that the

Fig. 6-2   Continuous position following system with smooth actuation.

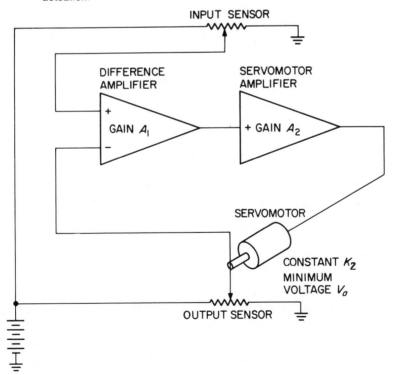

position error depends on the open-loop gain of the system. This analysis does not take dynamics into account. The output of the input-position sensor is related to the position by the constant K_1, viz. $e_{o1} = K_1 P_i$. Similarly, the voltage of the output-position sensor is $e_{o2} = K_1 P_o$. These voltages are fed to the differential amplifier, and the output signal (corresponding to the output position) is fed into the inverting input. The output of the differential amplifier is the difference of the voltages at its input, multiplied by the differential gain. The output of this stage is then fed to the power amplifier, which is used to drive the servomotor. The servomotor will turn until the voltage at its terminals is very small, and equal to V_a.

The position error is $P_i - P_o$. This position error produces an error voltage $K_1 e_{o1} - K_1 e_{o2}$. The torque of the servomotor is proportional to the product of the input voltage and the servomotor constant K_2. Thus, the torque of the servomotor is:

$$A_1 A_2 K_2 (K_1 e_{o1} - K_1 e_{o2})$$

When this is equal to V_a, the servomotor will cease motion:

$$V_a = A_1 A_2 K_1 K_2 (e_{o1} - e_{o2})$$
$$= A_1 A_2 K_1 K_2 (P_i - P_o)$$
$$P_i - P_o = \frac{V_a}{A_1 A_2 K_1 K_2}$$

V_a is the voltage at which the servomotor stops movement. Thus, the position error is related to the product of A_1, A_2, K_1, K_2, the servomotor constant. If the gain is large, the position error will be reduced.

VELOCITY AND SPEED CONTROLS

Velocity and speed are phenomena which lend themselves to control by electronic sensing methods. The transducers and sensors which relate speed or velocity to an electrical quantity are often called *tachometers*. Very often a tachometer will monitor the angular velocity of a rotating shaft.

A tachometer may be created by several means. It may be a small dc generator whose output voltage is proportional to the speed of shaft rotation. The field may be supplied by a permanent magnet. Another family of tachometers has a pulse output which is proportional to shaft speed. These tachometers usually produce one or more well-defined pulses for each revolution. If these pulses are counted and averaged over a time interval, the shaft velocity may be found. Since these pulses indicate the rate of revolution, they are a good indication of shaft speed. The pulses may be generated in a number of ways, the most popular being the inductive and the photoelectric methods. In the inductive method, a toothed wheel revolves in a magnetic field. As the wheel revolves, lines of flux are broken or twisted. These breaks or twists induce a voltage in a sensing coil, which is inserted into the magnetic field. To produce a high voltage, the coil is wound with many turns. If the wheel has N teeth, N pulses will be produced during each revolution. The shape of the pulses depends on the shape of the gear or toothed wheel used to produce them.

A simple photoelectric tachometer makes use of a disc interposed between a photoelectric cell and a light source. The disc, which is driven by a shaft, has alternate light and dark areas. As the shaft rotates, the light beam is alternately passed or broken. If the disc has N light areas, the light beam will be broken N times each revolution. Thus, N pulses will be produced each revolution.

One common use for tachometers is in the maintenance of a constant speed or shaft velocity. The output of the tachometer is compared to a reference voltage; the difference is taken and amplified by a differential amplifier. The resultant output is an error signal which may be used to correct the speed, assuming that the speed of the prime mover may be so controlled. This method may be easily applied when the tachometer output is dc but must be modified when using another type of tachometer. The modification involves converting the pulse-type output to a dc voltage. First, each pulse must have a fixed time duration. The period of the pulse should be much smaller than the period of the interval between pulses. Secondly, the voltage amplitude of each pulse should be constant from pulse to pulse, and also over long periods of time. These conditions may be met by using a monostable multivibrator for pulse shaping, where the tachometer's output signal is used only for triggering purposes. The shaped pulses are then fed to a low-pass filter, where all the high frequency components are removed, so that only the dc component remains. The low-pass filter may be as simple as a simple resistance–capacitance combination if the resistance–capacitance time constant is much larger than the period of the pulse interval. If the pulse width is τ_1 and the total period is τ_2, then the output of the low-pass filter will be $(V\tau_1)/\tau_2$, where V is the amplitude of the input pulse. If the pulses occur more frequently, the ratio of τ_1 to τ_2 increases. This means that the low-pass filter's output voltage will increase also. However, the frequency of the pulses is a function of the shaft velocity or speed. Thus, the output of the low-pass filter is proportional to the speed or velocity of the tachometer input.

If a resistance–capacitance integrator is used to remove the ac from the tachometer output, the speed control's response may be sluggish, or the control may fail to respond to rapid variations in the speed. This is because the time constant of the low-pass filter attenuates all variations in output speed which are higher in frequency than its cutoff frequency. As was the case with the position-following system, the error between the desired and the attained was proportional to the open-loop gain of the system. If the gains of the final actuator, the tachometer, and the difference amplifier are assumed to be reasonably flat in frequency response, then the open-loop gain will decrease at higher frequencies because of the effect of the low-pass filter. If the low-pass rolloff causes a 50 per cent reduction in open-loop gain at a certain frequency, then the possible shaft velocity error increases by the same percentage.

A simple constant-speed control (Fig. 6-3) consists of a tachometer, a difference amplifier, and a shunt-field dc motor. What type of motor is used is not important so long as the speed can be electrically controlled. The output of

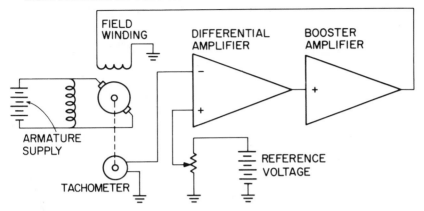

Fig. 6-3 Constant-motor-speed system block diagram.

the tachometer is a voltage which is proportional to shaft speed. This voltage is compared to a reference voltage derived from a potentiometer arm. The output of the amplifier is the amplified difference of the two input voltages. This is given a power boost by a booster amplifier fed from the output of the difference amplifier (because the difference amplifier's power output may be insufficient to drive the motor's field coil).

If the motor is running at a certain speed, and the load on it is increased, its shaft speed will tend to decrease. This decrease will cause a corresponding decrease in the tachometer output voltage. This voltage is subtracted from the reference voltage by the differential amplifier. The difference voltage becomes more negative because of the drop in tachometer voltage. Since the inverting terminal is becoming more negative with respect to the positive terminal, the net effect is a more positive output from the differential amplifier. The increased positive output increases the current in the field winding, which tends to increase the motor speed. To set a speed, the reference voltage is varied. There will always be a differential voltage at the amplifier input terminals. This differential voltage is required to maintain a quiescent current for the field winding.

To illustrate how the constant-speed parameters affect the performance as the load on the output is varied, we examine

the system of Fig. 6-4, which consists of a dc motor, a tachometer, a differential amplifier, and a reference voltage. The
idealized torque–speed characteristics are also shown for the
motor, which may be of the separately excited shunt-field
type or the permanent-magnet field type. The no-load speed
of the motor is directly proportional to the applied armature

Fig. 6-4   (a) Constant-motor-speed system block diagram;
(b) rpm of separately excited motor as a function of armature
voltage.

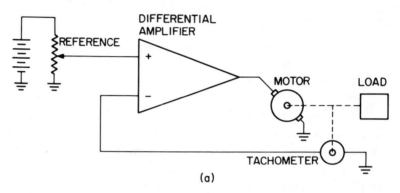

(a)

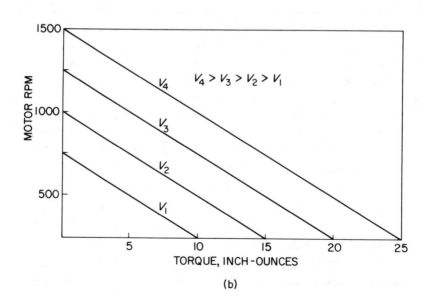

(b)

voltage. The addition of an output load causes the speed to drop until the motor stalls, or ceases to rotate. The equation relating motor speed, torque, and armature voltage may have the form

$$\text{Motor Speed} = \omega_m = (\omega_o)\frac{V_a}{V_o} - KT$$

where ω_m is the shaft speed, ω_o is the speed at no load when the armature voltage is V_o, V_a is the actual armature voltage, T is the torque delivered to the shaft, and K is the constant of proportionality. Referring to the graphed characteristics, at ± 1000 rpm, V_o is 50 volts. We note that for a 1000 rpm no-load speed, the motor will stall when a 15 inch-ounce load is applied. This fixes K as 66.7 inch-ounces per rpm.

To arrive at a mathematical determination of system performance the other constants must be assumed. The tachometer may be assumed to have a ten-volt output at 1000 rpm. Hence the tachometer constant is 0.01 volt per rpm. The amplifier may be assumed to have a gain of 1000. The first unknown is the reference voltage which must be used to set a speed of 1000 rpm, the base speed for our calculations. At no load, the torque–speed characteristics indicate an armature voltage of 50 volts for the 1000-rpm speed. This is also equal to the output voltage of the differential amplifier. This voltage is the difference between the tachometer voltage and the reference voltage, multiplied by the amplifier gain of 1000:

$$V_a = e_o = 1000\,(V_{ref} - V_{tach})$$
$$V_{tach} = K_t \text{ rpm} = (1000)\,(0.01) = 10 \text{ volts}$$
$$V_a = 50 = 1000\,(V_{ref} - 10)$$
$$V_{ref} - 10 = 0.05$$
$$V_{ref} = 10.05 \text{ volts}$$

The equation for motor speed with a fixed armature voltage is

$$\omega_m = \frac{1000}{50}V_a - 66.7T$$

which predicts that the motor speed would linearly decrease on an increase in load torque. If the armature voltage is not fixed, but instead is derived from the amplified difference between a tachometer voltage and a reference voltage, we have our constant-speed system. Substituting the amplifier output voltage for V_a, we have

$$\omega_m = \frac{1000}{50}[A_o(V_{ref} - K_t \text{ rpm})] - 66.7T$$

$$= 20.0 \ [1000(10.05 - 0.01\omega_m)] - 66.7T$$

$$\omega_m(200 + 1) = 20,000(10.05) - 66.7T$$

$$\omega_m = \frac{(20,000)(10.05) - 66.7T}{201}$$

$$= \frac{201,000}{201} - \frac{66.7T}{201}$$

$$= 1000 - 0.332T$$

The no-load speed is the same as before. However, the effect of a torque load has been decreased by a factor of 201. When the motor armature was supplied from a constant-voltage source, an applied load of 7.5 inch-ounces would have caused a 500 rpm drop in the motor speed. With the constant-speed system, the same torque load causes a speed drop of 2.5 rpm. The drop in speed from 1000 rpm to 997.5 rpm is so slight as to be almost insignificant when compared to the 500 rpm drop for the earlier case. Instead of giving specific examples, we can analytically find the improvement in performance to be expected. Starting with the motor-speed equation, we substitute the differential-amplifier output voltage for the armature voltage:

$$\text{Motor Speed} = \omega_m = \left(\frac{\omega_o}{V_o}\right)V_a - KT$$

$$V_a = e_o = A_o(V_{ref} - K_t\omega_m)$$

$$\omega_m = \frac{\omega_o}{V_o}[A_o(V_{ref} - K_t\omega_m)] - KT$$

$$\omega_m\left(1 + \frac{\omega_o}{V_o}A_oK_t\right) = \left(\frac{A_o\omega_o}{V_o}\right)V_{ref} - KT$$

$$\omega_m = \frac{(A_o\omega_o V_{ref}/V_o) - KT}{1 + (\omega_o/V_o)A_oK_t}$$

$$= \frac{A_o\omega_o V_{ref}/V_o}{1 + (\omega_o/V_o)A_oK_t} - \frac{KT}{1 + (\omega_o/V_o)A_oK_t}$$

$$= \frac{A_o\omega_o V_{ref}}{V_o + \omega_o A_oK_t} - \frac{KT}{1 + (\omega_o/V_o)A_oK_t}$$

For $T = 0$, $\omega_m = \omega_o$, and

$$\omega_m = \omega_o = \frac{A_o\omega_o V_{ref}}{V_o + \omega_o A_oK_t}$$

$$V_{ref} = \frac{V_o + \omega_o A_oK_t}{A_o}$$

The first equation relates the system parameters such as the tachometer constant, the amplifier gain, and the motor constants, to the performance. The major criterion for performance is, of course, the maintenance of constant motor speed. The first term of the equation expresses the performance of the motor at no load. From this term we can determine the necessary reference voltage which must be used to set a desired rpm. This is solved for in the second equation. The second term of the first equation accounts for the change in motor speed when a torque load is applied. When there was no feedback system and the motor was supplied from a constant voltage source, the corresponding term was just K_t. With feedback, K_t has been divided by a term which depends on the amplifier gain, the tachometer constant, and the motor constant. If this denominator is small, the torque has a large effect on motor speed. If it is made large, the speed of the shaft will resist changes imposed by applied torque loads. The equation predicts that by increasing the amplifier gain by a factor of ten, the speed regulation increases in roughly the same amount. If the gain is increased tenfold but the tachometer constant is decreased also by a factor of ten, the system performance will be the same. What may change is the reference voltage required to produce the same rpm. The denominator of the second term of the first equation, with the one removed, is called the gain of the system. The higher the gain, the better will the system performance be, under steady-state conditions.

An electronic sensing control is advantageously used to monitor the speed of motors and other moving devices, and to indicate excessive or insufficient speed. The response to the undesired condition may be a relay closure which signals an alarm, corrects the condition, or shuts off the power. A simple over- or under-speed control may use a tachometer to furnish a voltage proportional to the speed being monitored. This tachometer signal is then fed into one terminal of a comparator. The other terminal of the comparator is fed by a reference voltage. When the voltage furnished by the tachometer equals the reference voltage, the comparator changes state. Depending on the type of control needed, the tachometer voltage will be higher or lower than the reference voltage for normal operation. The comparator's output may be used to drive a relay. A small amount of hysteresis may be added to the comparator to provide snap action comparable to that obtained with a Schmitt trigger. A problem arises with this scheme at very low speeds, primarily because of the tachometer. There are two basic types of tachometers. One is actually a miniature dc generator whose field is supplied by permanent magnets. The armature voltage is directly proportional to the speed of the shaft rotation. At very slow rotations, the output voltage may become very low. Moreover, there will be considerable ripple in the output, even when a large number of poles is used. The other type of tachometer is a pulse generator. An average dc voltage dependent on shaft rotation is obtained here by integrating the pulses. At very low speeds, a very large time constant must be used to smooth the output. This type of tachometer tends to be sluggish, and is therefore generally unsuited for use in an over- or under-speed control, where fast response is desirable in most cases.

The problem is often resolved by using time measurement instead of speed measurements, which are a form of frequency measurements. That is, the period is monitored instead of the repetition rate. This technique is usually more successful at slow speeds. The basis for the under- or over-speed control, which is now actually an under- or over-length period control, is an accurately determined time. This time is often governed by the output pulse width of a monostable multivibrator. A typical circuit (see Fig. 6-5) uses two transistors and is fed by narrow pulses at a repetition rate determined by the monitored speed. The pulses may be generated by a mechanical switch, an electromagnetic pickup, or a photoelectric cell and light source. The only criterion

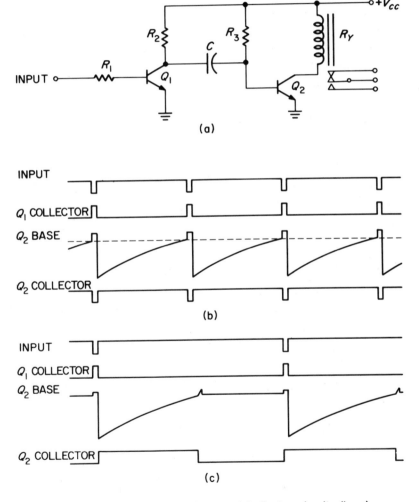

Fig. 6-5 (a) Motor under-speed indicator circuit; (b, c) waveforms for (b) satisfactory speed and (c) under-speed.

for the pulse is that it be very narrow in respect to its period. Assume that Q_2 is normally saturated because of the current flow through R_3. The collector of Q_1 is at the positive supply voltage, V_{cc}. The base of Q_2 is at $+0.6$ volt because of the saturation. Therefore, the capacitor is charged to $V_{cc} - 0.6$ volt, with the side connected to the collector of Q_1 positive. When the first input pulse appears on the input, Q_1 turns on. Its collector drops from V_{cc} to $V_{ce(sat)}$, which may be $+0.1$ volt. This voltage change is applied to the capacitor. Since the voltage across the capacitor cannot change instantaneously, the capacitor remains charged with $V_{cc} - 0.6$ volt. However, one side is now at $+0.1$ volt. That means that the side connected to the base of Q_2 is $(V_{cc} - 0.6) - 0.1$ volt below ground. Q_2 is thus cut off, and its collector current is zero. The relay coil is de-energized. After the passage of the pulse, the capacitor begins charging toward V_{cc} through R_3, with a time constant R_3C. If the next pulse arrives before the capacitor has a chance to charge up to $+0.6$ volt, Q_2 will not turn on fully. The short positive pulse at the collector of Q_1 will recharge the capacitor and turn on Q_2 momentarily. Once the pulse goes negative, Q_2 will again be cut off. However, the situation is different if the pulses arrive too slowly. The second transistor, Q_2, will again be cut off after the pulse. However, the capacitor will charge to 0.6 volt before the next input pulse arrives. The output of the transistor will fall before the input pulse arrives. If an end circuit is used at the output of the circuit and the input, the fact that the capacitor has charged up will be reflected in a wide output pulse. This means that the input pulses have been occurring too slowly, and thus that the motor or other device is going too slowly too. The comparison here is between tne time constant R_3C and the period of the input pulses. This type of circuit may be easily modified for use as an over-frequency or over-speed control.

PRESSURE CONTROLS

Electronic pressure controls are used to monitor, regulate,

and control the absolute or differential pressure in a controllable area. Their principal advantages over purely mechanical controls are greater ease in setting the actuation point and the feasibility of prompt operation. Once the pressure signal is converted to an electrical signal it may be easily transmitted over long distances.

There are two commonly used pressure sensors. The first type uses a metal bellows which converts a differential pressure to a mechanical displacement. The bellows is a linear transducer, and its extension under pressure is analagous to a spring's extension under tension and contraction under compression. The movement of the bellows is coupled mechanically to the wiper arm of a potentiometer so that the pressure controls the position of the wiper arm. When a voltage is applied to the end points of the potentiometer, a voltage proportional to the pressure is produced.

The second type of pressure sensor uses strain gauges instead of a potentiometer. The pressure is applied to a thin metal diaphragm. Under pressure, the diaphragm bulges. The stress on the diaphragm is equal to the pressure across it divided by the area. For small values of stress, the resultant strain, or elongation, is related to the stress by a constant known as Young's modulus. Thus, the strain produced in the diaphragm is proportional to the stress, which is proportional to the pressure across the diaphragm. This strain causes the resistance of a strain gauge to change. The strain gauge is bonded to the metal diaphragm. A pair of gauges may be used, bonded to the diaphragm perpendicular to one another. For each gauge which is bonded to the diaphragm, another gauge may be included in the housing to serve as a dummy gauge. This dummy gauge is not under strain, and merely serves to compensate for resistance changes due to ambient temperature. The gauges are usually connected in a Wheatstone bridge arrangement with all four leads brought out.

Each of the transducers has its advantages and disadvantages. The potentiometer control offers a high output voltage, and its linearity can be improved by trimming the sensing potentiometer. However, because of its mechanical movement, the sensor is prone to shock and vibration errors. Also, if there is a great deal of repetitive pressure variation, the mechanism may tend to wear out from friction and metal fatigue. The principal disadvantage of the strain-gauge sensor is the low output signal, which makes some form of amplification and signal conditioning mandatory before it may be used. However, it is less susceptible to shock and vibration. Because there are no moving parts, its expected life is greater than that of the potentiometer control. Its internal resonances will generally be higher in frequency than those of the potentiometer sensor.

To implement a pressure control, some form of decision-making circuit such as a comparator may be used (see Fig. 6-6). The comparator may be used to drive a relay, or it may drive an electrically operated valve directly. When a pressure regulator is required, the control may be used in a negative-feedback loop, using perhaps a differential amplifier, a servo-valve, and a reference voltage. When a strain-gauge control is used, signal conditioning must be included. The output of a typical strain-gauge sensor may be one to two millivolts per volt of applied voltage at full scale. This means that when ten volts are supplied to the Wheatstone bridge, the maximum output voltage will be ten to twenty millivolts. An adjustment is often made to the Wheatstone bridge in order to "zero" it (that is, the output from the bridge should be zero when the applied pressure is zero). Because of the high values of gain necessary to use the transducer, the bridge is often excited with ac. The amplified ac signal, which is virtually drift free, can be demodulated to yield dc. A typical pressure-control system may include an indicator like those used for temperature controls. Such a system might consist of a strain-gauge pressure sensor fed from an ac source, amplified by a stable amplifier, filtered, and then demodulated by a detector. The resultant dc may then be used to drive a meter for an indication of pressure. It may also be used to drive a differential amplifier for the maintenance of a constant pressure. The output actuator for the constant-pressure regulator may be either a servovalve or a solenoid-operated valve. Servovalves allow a continuous variation in valve opening, whereas solenoid valves usually operate fully open or fully shut. Like other regulation systems, the degree of regulation depends on the amount of gain available in the negative-feedback path.

Pressure-sensing controls may operate on absolute pressure, gauge pressure, or differential pressure. All of these terms are generally expressed in pounds per square inch, abbreviated psi. Absolute pressure is, as its name implies, a measure that does not depend on the pressure at sea level or some other quantity. The absolute pressure of a vacuum, for example, is zero. The absolute pressure at sea level is approximately

Fig. 6-6 Pressure control and indicator system using strain-gauge pressure sensor, ac amplifier, filter, and demodulator as signal conditioning, and using the differential amplifier to drive actuator.

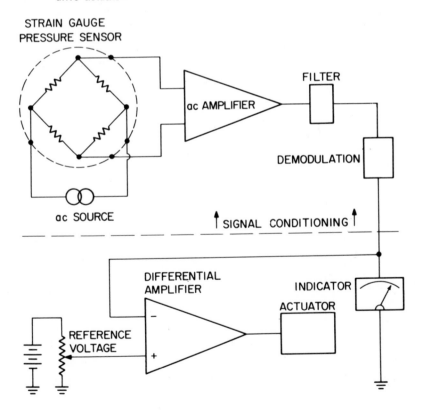

14.7 psi. It is established practice to add a letter to the pressure to indicate whether the measured pressure is absolute, gauge, or differential. Thus, 14.7 psi absolute pressure is abbreviated 14.7 psia. Gauge pressure refers to pressure differences from the atmospheric pressure at sea level. Thus, 14.7 psia is zero gauge pressure. Both negative and positive gauge pressures are possible because the absolute pressure can be above or below 14.7 psia. Gauge pressures carry the suffix g, for example, 10 psig. Differential pressure is the pressure difference between two points, both of which can be at arbitrary pressures. It is abbreviated psid. Most pressure measurements imply gauge pressure when no other information is given.

ULTRASONIC AND ACOUSTIC CONTROLS

The uses of mechanical input sensing controls are not necessarily limited to applications involving physical motion. There are a number of areas where controls using vibration excel. The amount of movement may be as little as a few thousandths of an inch, so there may be some justification in calling the controls motionless.

The vibratory control may use a liquid- or solid-level sensor (see Fig. 6-7). The level sensor consists of a vibration transmitter, a vibration sensor, and an amplifier. The vibration sensor drives the amplifier, which in turn drives the vibration transmitter. If there is a solid or liquid material between the transmitter and the sensor, the vibrations are easily coupled between them. The gain of the amplifier is adjusted so that the gain from the vibration sensor, through the amplifier, through the vibration transmitter, and through the media, is greater than one. With proper phasing, the polarity of the gain is positive. Thus, since there is positive feedback with unity gain, oscillations will be sustained. The rate of oscillation will be determined by the system parameters; typically they may be in the ultrasonic region. This oscillation is detected and provides a dc output voltage. The situation changes when a solid or liquid is not present be-

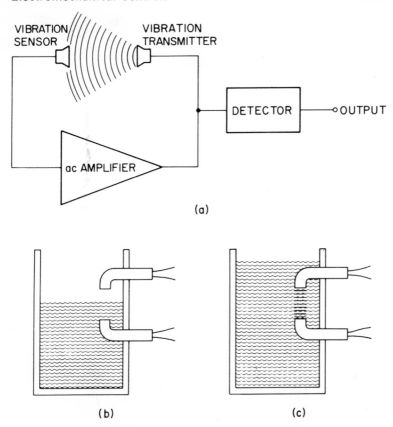

Fig. 6-7 (a) Acoustic level control block diagram and side view of installation; (b) no oscillations; (c) sustained oscillations because material between heads affords excellent acoustic coupling.

tween the sensor and the transmitter. The acoustic signal passing through space is greatly attenuated, because the air is not an efficient sound conductor. The total gain of the system drops to below unity, and oscillations can no longer be sustained. The detected dc voltage drops to zero, indicating that there is no longer any sound-conducting material between the sensing and transmitting heads. Both heads must be mechanically isolated from each other or they may have enough coupling to sustain oscillation. This type of control is very similar to the photocell and light source combination. While the circuitry involved here may be a trifle more complicated, the control is not affected by dirt or the opacity of the material. For example, a photocell and light source sensor might have trouble distinguishing a crystal-clear liquid from air. The ultrasonic control has no such problem.

Another area where vibratory controls are very useful is in gauging thickness (see Fig. 6-8a). The basic thickness con-

Fig. 6-8 (a) Acoustic thickness control block diagram gauges thickness by setting up acoustic standing wave in material. (b) first, second, and third standing wave patterns produced in material.

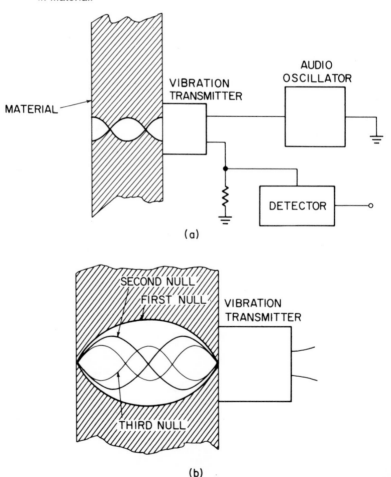

trol uses a vibration transmitter coupled to the material to be gauged. Acoustic standing waves are induced in the material. The wavelength of the vibration in the material depends on the type of material, and on the speed of sound in it. The wavelength $\lambda = C/f$, where C is the speed of sound in the material, and f is the frequency of the applied vibration. If the wavelength is equal to exactly one-half, or an integral multiple of a half, there will be a node at the far side of the material. The acoustic power that is applied will be largely absorbed. If the power drawn by the transmitter is measured, the power will suddenly increase when the half wavelength is reached. To look at the situation in another way, the impedance of the transmitter will drop sharply at the half-wavelength point. This point can be easily detected electrically. The transmitter may be driven from a low-impedance voltage source. A resistor is inserted in series with the transmitter. When the impedance drops, the total series resistance drops, and the current in the circuit increases. This causes an increased voltage drop across the resistor. The voltage across the resistor may be amplified and demodulated to provide a dc output. This output is then available for control purposes.

The wavelength at which the null occurs is $\lambda = C/f$. But since the null may occur at an integral number of half wavelengths, this expression must be modified so that $\lambda = (nC)/(2f)$ where 2 is an allowance for half wavelengths, and n may be an integer. The thickness of the material corresponds to the lowest frequency at which a null may be found. The standing-wave patterns for the first, second, and third nulls are shown in Fig. 6-8b.

7

Feedback Sensing Controls

Negative feedback is an essential attribute of almost all electronic circuitry and electronic sensing controls. Feedback implies that something from the output of a circuit or system is applied at the input. If there is negative feedback, the output fed back will reduce the input signal, tending to reduce the output. The advantage of feedback is that the output may be constrained to closely follow the input. Nonlinearities in the amplifier or system are largely cancelled.

ELECTRONIC FEEDBACK

Some basic properties of feedback and its applications are most easily seen in studying the use of negative feedback in electronic circuitry. The main reason is that the circuits lend themselves to analysis and experimental verification. The results will be applicable in a broad range of uses.

For analysis we start with an amplifier whose basic parameters are a gain A, an input impedance Z_i, and an output impedance Z_o. We will assume that the amplifier's phase

165

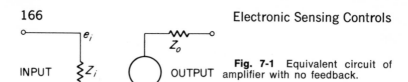

Fig. 7-1 Equivalent circuit of amplifier with no feedback.

shift is zero and that its frequency response is unlimited. If a signal were applied to its input terminal, that signal, multiplied by the gain A, would appear at the output, if the amplitude were not greater than the amplifier could deliver. The output impedance and the load impedance, acting as a voltage divider, cut down the output voltage delivered by the amplifier to R_1/Z_o times the unloaded output voltage. The equivalent circuit for this amplifier shows its parameters (see Fig. 7-1).

To add negative feedback, we feed the output voltage to a feedback network (see Fig. 7-2). This network may have active, passive, or combinations of both elements. The transfer function of the output voltage through this network is given the symbol β. The output of the network is then fed to a difference circuit where it is subtracted from the input signal. The input signal at the amplifier terminals is the

Fig. 7-2 Amplifier with negative feedback applied with β-network and difference circuit.

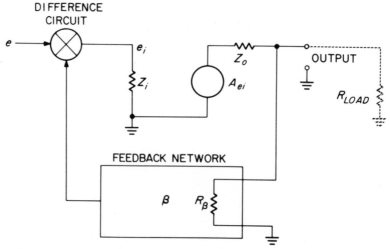

applied input signal minus the signal at the output of the β-network. The output voltage is then

$$e_o = \frac{A e_i R_L}{R_L + Z_o}$$

because $R\beta$ is assumed to be large with respect to R_L. Also,

$$e_i = -\beta e_o + e$$

$$= \frac{-A e_i R_L}{R_L + Z_o} (\beta) + e$$

$$e_i \left(1 + \frac{A R_L \beta}{R_L + Z_o} \right) = e$$

$$e_i = \frac{e}{1 + \dfrac{A \beta R_L}{R_L + Z_o}}$$

$$e_o = \frac{e A R_L}{(R_L + Z_o) \left(1 + \dfrac{A \beta R_L}{R_L + Z_o} \right)}$$

Rearranging terms,

$$e_o = e \left(\frac{A R_L}{R_L + Z_o + A \beta R_L} \right)$$

Dividing through by R_L,

$$e_o = e \left(\frac{A}{1 + Z_o/R_L + A \beta} \right)$$

Since the gain is defined as the ratio of the output voltage to the input voltage, the gain of the amplifier with feedback is

$$A_o = \frac{A}{1 + Z_o/R_L + A \beta}$$

Dividing by A,

$$A_o = \frac{1}{1/A + Z_o/R_L A + \beta}$$

The gain without feedback is referred to as the open-loop gain, or A. The gain with feedback is termed the closed-loop gain and is symbolized by A_o. According to the above equation, the closed-loop gain depends on the open-loop gain, the output and load impedances, and the transfer function of the feedback network β. If the open-loop gain is large, the first two terms in the denominator may be neglected, so that the gain is given by $1/\beta$. Although the resultant gain of the amplifier has been reduced by feedback, it is now primarily a function of β. The characteristics of the amplifier, principally gain and impedances, are usually widely varying and unstable. However, the characteristics of the β-network may be selected for extreme stability. This gives the gain of the amplifier essentially the same stability as the β-network.

Besides modifying the gain, negative feedback changes the output impedance. Without feedback, the output impedance is merely Z_o. This is the value the load resistance would have to have in order to reduce the output voltage to one-half its original value when unloaded. Examining the equation for the gain of the amplifier with feedback, we see that, to reduce the output voltage to one-half its original value, we could increase the value of the second term in the denominator. In fact, if this term were equal to the third term, the gain would be reduced by one-half. Thus, when the load resistance is equal to the amplifier's output impedance,

$$\beta = \frac{Z_o}{AR_L}$$

Solving for R_L,

$$R_L = \frac{Z_o}{A\beta}$$

The output impedance is seen to be reduced by a factor of $A\beta$ below what it was without feedback. Similarly, the input impedance is increased by a factor of $A\beta$. The low output impedance and high input impedance are qualities which are usually valued in voltage amplification.

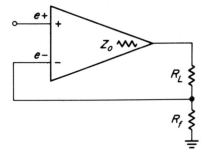

Fig. 7-3 Amplifier with current feedback.

It may be that characteristics desired in an amplifier are high input impedance and high output impedance. This is often found when working with currents instead of voltages. Instead of obtaining this condition with voltage feedback, it is achieved with current feedback. In a current feedback scheme, a voltage proportional to the output current is fed back to the input. This has the effect of stabilizing or limiting the output current. It also tends to increase the effective output impedance and increase the input impedance. A typical amplifier with current feedback is shown in Fig. 7-3; it uses a differential amplifier for subtraction of the feedback voltage. The voltage source in the amplifier has a value of $A(e^+ - e^-)$, where e^+ is the voltage at the positive, or noninverting, terminal, and e^- is the voltage at the negative, or inverting, terminal. This voltage produces a current flow of $e_o/(R_L + R_f + Z_o)$, where Z_o is the output impedance, R_L is the load impedance, and R_f is the feedback resistance. The voltage fed back into the inverting terminal is the product of the current flow and the feedback resistor,

$$e^- = \frac{R_f e_o}{R_L + R_f + Z_o}$$

The resultant output voltage is

$$A(e^+ - e^-) = e_o$$

$$e_o = A\left(e_i - \frac{e_o R_f}{R_L + R_f + Z_o}\right)$$

$$e_o\left(1 + \frac{A R_f}{R_f + R_L + Z_o}\right) = A e_i$$

$$e_o = \frac{A e_i}{1 + \dfrac{A R_f}{R_f + R_L + Z_o}}$$

Thus the voltage gain of the circuit is

$$A_o = \frac{A}{1 + \dfrac{A R_f}{R_f + R_L + Z_o}}$$

$$= \frac{1}{\dfrac{1}{A} + \dfrac{R_f}{R_f + R_L + Z_o}}$$

For very large values of A,

$$A_o = \frac{1}{\dfrac{R_f}{R_f + R_L + Z_o}}$$

$$= \frac{R_f + R_L + Z_o}{R_f}$$

The net gain from the input to the load resistance is

$$\frac{A_o R_L}{R_f + R_L + Z_o}$$

or

$$A = \frac{(R_f + R_L + Z_o) R_L}{(R_f + R_L + Z_o) R_f} = \frac{R_L}{R_f} = \beta$$

It can be shown that the output impedance is equal to the amplifier's output impedance multiplied by $(1 + \beta A)$. Similarly, the input impedance is the intrinsic input impedance increased by the same factor.

The effect of feedback is to make an amplifier's gain essentially independent of its internal parameters and dependent on the characteristics of the feedback network. This can only hold when the open-loop gain is considerably greater than the gain with feedback. When the feedback network has a gain of unity, the full output signal is fed back into the input. This is called unity feedback. Amplifiers with unity feedback have a gain of unity. This can be verified by substituting unity for β in any equation for the gain of an amplifier with feedback. One of the most familiar unity-feedback amplifiers is the emitter or cathode follower. It was analyzed in Chapter 3, and the input impedance was found to be increased by the factor β and the output impedance decreased by the same amount. Unity feedback is often used in amplifiers or systems where the gain is of little importance, and the linearizing properties of feedback are desired.

Feedback also affects the frequency response of an amplifier or system. If the bandwidth of an amplifier is defined as the frequency difference between the two points at which the voltage gain is reduced by 3 db, then the gain–bandwidth product of the amplifier may be defined as the product of the midband gain and the bandwidth.

The function of feedback is to maintain a constant gain–bandwidth product. That is, if we apply negative feedback to an amplifier with a high gain but a low bandwidth, we may decrease the gain and increase the bandwidth, but the product of gain and bandwidth will be constant in both cases. For example, consider the amplifier in Fig. 7-4. This two-stage amplifier consists of a common-emitter stage and a common-collector stage. The gain, which has a negative polarity, is realized in the first stage. The second stage acts as a buffer and an impedance transformer. Negative feedback may be applied by throwing the switch to the feedback position. It may be removed by placing the switch in the grounded position. The capacitor between the collector of Q_1 and ground will tend to decrease the gain of the amplifier at higher frequencies. For analysis, we will work with ac terms only, neglecting the dc terms and the biasing considerations. The transistors are assumed to have a β of 100.

First we will find the gain of the amplifier without feedback. The current in the base of Q_1 due to V_i is $V_i/600\Omega$. This produces a collector current βi_b, or $100\ (V_i/600\Omega)$. The collector voltage is the collector current multiplied by the impedance in the collector lead. This has three components.

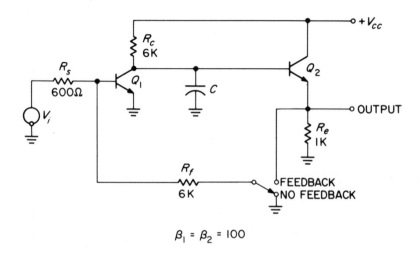

Fig. 7-4 Amplifier circuit with switch to connect or disconnect feedback network. Analysis shows that the product of gain and bandwidth is a constant and does not depend on feedback.

Two are resistive, the collector load resistor and the reflected emitter resistance of the common-collector stage. Assuming a β of 100, the reflected emitter resistance is over $100K$, and may be neglected when in shunt with the collector load resistor. The third component is the shunting effect of the capacitor. Thus, the impedance seen at the collector lead is the parallel combination of the collector load resistor and the capacitor, which is

$$\frac{1}{j\omega C + \frac{1}{6}K} = \frac{6K\Omega}{6Kj\omega C + 1}$$

The output voltage of the first stage is the product of the

collector impedance and the collector current. This is also the output voltage of the amplifier, since the common-collector stage has unity gain. The output voltage will have a negative sign because of the inversion produced in the first stage. Thus the output voltage is

$$100 \frac{-V_i}{600\Omega} \left(\frac{6K\Omega}{6Kj\omega C + 1} \right) = \frac{-V_i(1000)}{6Kj\omega C + 1}$$

The voltage gain is

$$A = \frac{V_o}{V_i} = \frac{1000}{6Kj\omega C + 1}$$

The denominator of the gain expression contains a real and a complex term. At low frequencies, the complex term is small, and the gain of the amplifier is one thousand. When the imaginary term in the denominator is equal to one, the gain has decreased by 3 decibels. This is the bandwidth of the amplifier without feedback.

If the feedback switch is now thrown to the other position, feedback will be applied. The input current at the base of Q_1 will be: $V_i/600 + V_o/6000$, where the first term is due to the input signal source and the second term is due to the voltage fed back. This base current is amplified by β and is impressed across the collector load impedance, $6000/(1 + 6Kj\omega C)$. The resultant collector voltage is

$$V_c = -\beta \left(\frac{V_i}{600} + \frac{V_o}{6000} \right) \left(\frac{6000}{1 + 6Kj\omega C} \right)$$

$$= V_o = \frac{-\beta V_o}{1 + 6Kj\omega C} - \frac{\beta V_i(10)}{1 + 6Kj\omega C}$$

Rearranging,

$$V_o \left(\frac{1 + \beta}{1 + 6Kj\omega C} \right) = \frac{-\beta V_i(10)}{1 + 6Kj\omega C}$$

$$V_o = \frac{\dfrac{V_i\beta(10)}{1 + 6Kj\omega C}}{1 + \dfrac{\beta}{1 + 6Kj\omega C}} = \frac{V_i\beta(10)}{\beta + 1 + 6Kj\omega C}$$

Fig. 7-5 (a) Equivalent circuit of unity feedback amplifier with nonlinear load resistance; (b) graph of resistance of load as a function of applied voltage; (c—opposite) graph of input voltage versus time of feedback amplifier; (d) graph of voltage versus time of amplifier; (e) graph of voltage delivered by voltage source of amplifier, showing how amplifier compensates for nonlinear load and keeps the output waveform identical to the input waveform.

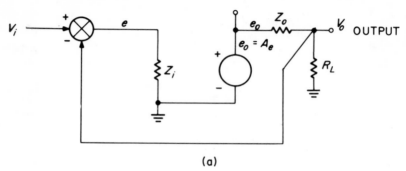

(a)

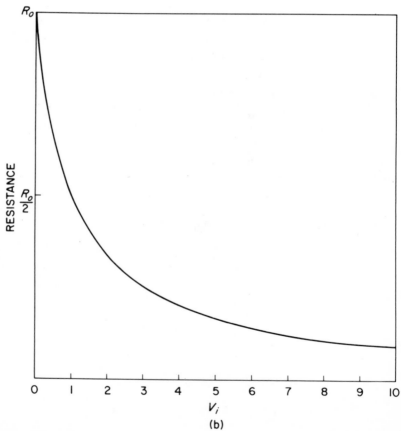

(b)

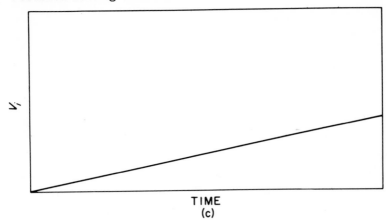

TIME
(c)

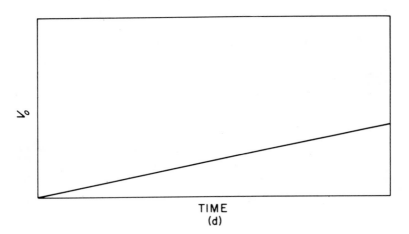

TIME
(d)

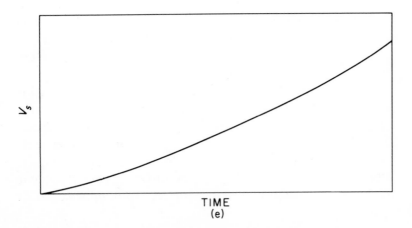

TIME
(e)

Since $\beta = 100$,

$$V_o = \frac{V_i\,(1000)}{100 + 1 + 6Kj\omega C}$$

and

$$A = \frac{V_o}{V_i} = \frac{1000}{101 + 6Kj\omega C}$$

The expression for the gain with feedback has both a real and imaginary term in its denominator. For low frequencies, the imaginary term is small compared to 101, and can be neglected. The gain is thus 1000/101, or approximately ten. The break point in the frequency response will occur when the real term and the imaginary term are equal. This is when $|6Kj\omega C| = 101$. The bandwidth of the other amplified corresponded to the point where $|6Kj\omega C| = 1$. It is evident that the break point of the amplifier with feedback is approximately one hundred times greater than the break point without feedback. The product of the gain and the bandwidth has remained constant.

As we have said previously, the effect of feedback is to make the output closely correspond to the input. The need for such a device arises when there are nonlinearities either in the amplifier, or in the load to be driven. Although the output follows the input, the intermediate stages may operate with a distorted replica of the input. These distortions are necessary in order to have a distortion-free output signal. For example, let us consider an amplifier with voltage feedback driving a nonlinear load resistance (see Fig. 7-5). The resistance is voltage sensitive, and it follows the equation $R = R_o/(1 + V/V')$, where R is the resistance, R_o is the resistance with no voltage applied, V' is the applied voltage necessary for the resistance to halve, and V is the applied voltage. While there may be no nonlinear resistance with this exact characteristic, many types of nonlinear, voltage-sensitive resistors exist. The voltage driving the feedback amplifier, which has unity feedback, is a ramp voltage with the form $V = aT$, where a is the slope and T is the elapsed time from some point of reference in time. The equivalent circuit of the amplifier consists of an input impedance Z_i, an output impedance Z_o, and an open-loop voltage gain A. We will assume that we can observe the voltage at the output of the equivalent circuit's voltage source, as well as the output and input voltages. Then the effect of the nonlinear load on the internal operation of the amplifier can be seen. The value of the voltage source is A times the input voltage, or $e_o = A (V_i - V_o)$. The fraction of the voltage source's voltage appearing at the output terminal is $(e_o R_L)/(R_L + Z_o) = V_o$, which is the output voltage delivered to the load resistance. Solving for the output voltage as a function of the input voltage, we have

$$V_o = \frac{e_o R_L}{R_L + Z_o} = \frac{A (V_i - V_o) R_L}{R_L + Z_o}$$

$$V_o \left(\frac{1 + A R_L}{R_L + Z_o} \right) = \frac{A V_i R_L}{R_L + Z_o}$$

$$V_o = \frac{\dfrac{V_i A R_L}{R_L + Z_o}}{1 + \dfrac{A R_L}{R_L + Z_o}}$$

$$= \frac{V_i A R_L}{R_L + Z_o + A R_L}$$

Dividing through by A, we have

$$V_o = \frac{V_i R_L}{\dfrac{R_L + Z_o}{A} + R_L}$$

Assuming A is very large,

$$V_o = \frac{V_i R_L}{0 + R_L} = V_i$$

Thus the output waveform will follow the input fairly independently of the value of the load resistance, if the open-loop gain is high enough. The voltage produced by the voltage source is related to the output voltage as follows:

$$V_o = \frac{e_o R_L}{R_L + Z_o}$$

so that
$$e_o = \frac{V_o(R_L + Z_o)}{R_L}$$

But
$$R_L = \frac{R_o}{1 + V/V'} \quad \text{and if } V = V_o$$

then,
$$R_L = \frac{R_o}{1 + V_o/V'}$$

Substituting,

$$e_o = V_o \frac{\left(\dfrac{R_o}{1 + V_o/V'} + Z_o \right)}{\left(\dfrac{R_o}{1 + V_o/V'} \right)}$$

Simplifying,

$$e_o = V_o \left(\frac{R_o + Z_o + Z_o V_o/V'}{R_o} \right)$$

$$= V_o \left(1 + \frac{Z_o}{R_o} + \frac{Z_o V_o}{R_o V'} \right)$$

Setting $Z_o = R_o/10$,

$$e_o = V_o \left(1.1 + \frac{V_o}{10V'} \right) = 1.1 V_o + \frac{V_o^2}{10V'}$$

This feedback corrects for the nonlinearity of the load resistance by forcing the source voltage, e_o, to be nonlinear also.

It is seen that the voltage at the output of the voltage source has a quadratic term, while the input and output voltages closely correspond to each other. There is no distortion evident at the output of the amplifier, yet the output of the voltage source is forced to increase at a rate greater than the input rate. The amplifier is forced to distort the signal internally so that the output will follow the input. If there were a nonlinear component within the amplifier, its distorting effect would also be removed by the action of the negative feedback. Conversely, if there is any nonlinearity in the feedback path, the output of the amplifier will not follow the input, but will be distorted.

We can summarize the important effects of negative feedback. First, the impedance levels of the amplifier will be changed. The gain–bandwidth product will remain constant, but the bandwidth may increase if the gain has been decreased. The effect of feedback is to linearize the amplifier so that nonlinearities are cancelled. This is true of internal or external nonlinearities. However, a nonlinearity in the feedback path will create distortion. The overall effect of feedback is to improve the performance, and make the performance more predictable.

FEEDBACK IN SENSING CONTROLS

The application of negative feedback is not limited to all electronic circuits such as amplifiers. Rather, feedback may be successfully employed in a large number of areas with the same type of advantages as are obtained with electronic feedback. Specifically, feedback may be used with advantage in all types of electronic sensing controls. The purpose of the feedback may be to linearize an automatic control system, to allow its performance to be easily predicted, or to improve its degree of performance.

Negative feedback implies that a portion of the system's output is fed back to the input where it can modify the performance. In the course of discussing many types of electronic sensing controls, we have introduced many systems which were dependent on negative feedback for their operation. Among them were constant-temperature systems, position-following systems, and constant-speed systems. Each form of electronic sensing control employed negative feedback either to improve the regulation, or to hold some quantity constant, or to minimize some error. Although there is no need for a negative-feedback system to use electronic circuitry, the fact that the control was in the electronic domain made the application of feedback very easy. This is because of the easily attainable high gains and the simplicity of mathematical manipulations, such as taking sums and differences.

The block diagram of an electronic sensing control with eedback applied would show a sensor, the appropriate electronics, and an output actuator. The actuator would act in such a manner as to affect the input upon which the sensor was functioning. There is a loop from the input sensor through the electronic circuitry, through the output actuator, back to the controlled phenomena, and finally back to the input sensor. This comprises the negative-feedback loop. The loop can be broken at any point, and a signal can be introduced. It can even be broken within the controlled phenomena, between the input sensor and the output actuator. If a signal is introduced, a corresponding response will appear at the other side of the break. The dimensions of the signal at either side of the break will be similar. The ratio of the signal that is introduced to the resultant signal is the open-loop gain of the system. If the feedback through the system is unity feedback, the closed-loop gain of the system will be unity, regardless of where the loop is broken. This implies that the transfer function for the signal fed back is unity. While it is possible to produce systems where the gain is greater than unity, these are rarely found outside of servo-mechanical systems.

An electronic sensing control with feedback may be analyzed just as electronic amplifiers with feedback were analyzed. In sensing-control systems where either the output is to remain constant, or the error is to be minimized, the open-loop gain is the prime parameter. For steady-state conditions, the open-loop gain allows the prediction of performance. For example, if a particular system had an open-loop gain of 100, we would expect that the regulation would be 100 times better than the regulation of the system without feedback. However, the feedback is only useful when all the system's components are operating in the linear regions. For a pressure control system which employs feedback, the main components are a pressure sensor, an amplifier, and an output actuator. If any of these components saturates, the system will no longer be able to maintain regulation, because an output is called for which cannot be accommodated by the system. Saturation means that the equations of performance are no longer valid because they were based on the assumption of linearity. The analysis of the performance of the sensing control does not have to be limited to the electronic part. The transfer function from the output actuator back to the input sensor may be theoretically derived or experimentally determined. Once this information is obtained, the performance of the sensing control may be calculated.

The transient response of the electronic circuitry, the input sensor, and the output actuator are all important to the transient response of the system. An important part of the transient response is determined by the controlled phenomena. Occasionally the external pieces of the system may introduce such large time constants that these time constants predominate. A good example of this is seen in constant-temperature controls. Often the thermal lag in heating or cooling a certain volume is far greater than any other lag. Therefore, this lag is the lag which is noticed the most in the transient response of the system, and it will be this lag which determines the speed of any action or response to an applied command.

In all of our previous discussions of negative feedback we have neglected the transient response of systems or amplifiers which had negative feedback applied. Only the steady state was treated. However, there is considerable reason to investigate the effect of transient response, even when we are concerned principally with steady-state operation. The reason for this is that the closed-loop system may not be stable with feedback, and it may oscillate or be unresponsive to commands. The reason for the instability cannot be found in the steady-state analysis. Rather, the answer lies in analyzing the transient conditions. The steady-state equations do not give any hint that the negative feedback can turn into positive feedback which will cause oscillations. This reversal in polarity is due to excessive phase shifts in the feedback loop. We noticed that there could be instabilities in the thermostatically controlled temperature controller. This was evidenced by the controlled temperature's periodic excursions above and below the set point. The reason for these periodic oscillations was the thermal-lag inherent in the system. These instabilities will now be discussed.

STABILITY OF FEEDBACK
SENSING CONTROLS

The application of negative feedback to electronic sensing controls has numerous advantages. The performance of such controls may be much greater than the performance of controls not using feedback. There is, however, one problem associated with feedback controls. It may be possible for the polarity of the feedback to reverse at some extreme point in the control's range. Even though this point may never actually be reached in normal operation, the positive feedback will cause oscillation to be sustained. This oscillation will interfere with the normal functioning of the control in most cases. It is this instability which limits the amount of gain which may be applied in a negative-feedback loop. For if there were no penalties for increasing gain, the gain would always be high in order to minimize errors and improve performance.

The problem of instability may be observed qualitatively. The system under discussion may be a constant motor-speed system such as was described in Chapter 6. That system employed a separately excited shunt motor, a tachometer, a differential amplifier, and a reference voltage. The tachometer signal was compared to the reference voltage by the differential amplifier. The amplified difference was used to furnish the motor's armature voltage. The gain of the system was found, as well as the effect of feedback on the torque load. If we take this system from a standing start, or from a certain speed, and then suddenly change the desired speed, we observe that the motor's speed will not change instantaneously. Instead, the change will take a certain amount of time. The reason for this time lag is the fact that the rotating motor and tachometer are storing energy because of their inertia. This stored energy, which is a function of the speed of rotation, cannot be changed instantaneously without the expenditure of infinite power. Since this is impossible, the observed lag between command and performance is necessary. Instead of applying a sudden, single change in the command, we can apply a sinusoidal change, with the resultant sinusoidal variation in output speed. Because of the lag, it may be possible for the system's response to be out of step with the command. Thus, suppose that a command to speed up rotation has, after a lag, succeeded in speeding up the rotation. Because of the inverse feedback, the signal fed back will tend to slow down the rotation. However, suppose that, because of the lag in the system, this signal fed back to slow down rotation arrives at the same time as a command to slow down rotation. Instead of cancelling each other out, the two signals add to produce a larger signal to reduce the output. It can be seen that if there is enough gain and lag in the system, the command signal will be augmented by the signal fed back instead of being reduced by it. This requires a sufficient time delay in the response of the system as well. This condition is clearly oscillitory. The oscillations may be stopped either by reducing the gain of the system, or by reducing the magnitude of the time lag. The detailed analysis of transient response and stability is beyond the scope of this book. However, a look at the analagous problem in purely electronic circuitry may be instructive.

An electronic analog of the constant-speed system consists of a differential amplifier, a reference supply, and a simulated

Fig. 7-6 Electronic analog of constant-speed system with two time delays.

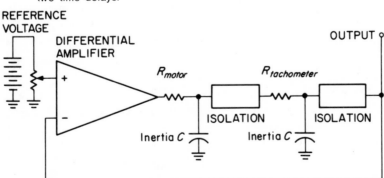

tachometer and motor (see Fig. 7-6). The inertia of the tachometer and the motor are simulated by electronic energy storage elements (capacitors). Just as the speed of an object with inertia cannot change instantaneously, the voltage across the capacitor cannot change instantaneously. Assuming both time constants identical, the open-loop gain of the system is

$$\frac{A}{(1 + j\omega RC)^2}$$

where A is the amplifier gain and RC is the time constant R–C of the networks. If the loop is now closed with unity negative feedback, the closed-loop gain is

$$\frac{A}{1 + A} = \frac{\dfrac{A}{(1 + j\omega RC)^2}}{1 + \dfrac{A}{(j\omega RC + 1)^2}}$$

$$= \frac{A}{(j\omega RC + 1)^2 + A}$$

Multiplying out the denominator we have

$$\frac{A}{A + (1 + j^2\omega^2 R^2 C^2 + 2j\omega RC)}$$

or

$$\frac{A}{A + 1 - \omega^2 R^2 C^2 + j2\omega RC}$$

The denominator is composed of a real and an imaginary part. If the denominator approaches zero or becomes positive, the amplifier will become unstable and will oscillate. It can be shown that the amplifier will be unstable if its gain decreases with frequency at a rate of 12 db per octave when the value of the gain is zero. These conditions are met with the two resistance–capacitance networks, because each network contributes a slope of 6 db per octave.

Index

Index